MATHS AND HISTORY

MATHS and the Egyptians

Written by John Davis

HOPSCOTCH
EDUCATIONAL PUBLISHING

Contents

Published by Hopscotch Educational Publishing Ltd, Unit 2, The Old Brushworks, 56 Pickwick Road, Corsham, Wiltshire SN13 9BX
Tel: 01249 701701

© 2002 Hopscotch Educational Publishing

Written by John Davis
Series design by Blade Communications
Illustrated by Bernard Connors
Cover illustration by Virginia Grey
Printed by Hobbs the Printers Ltd

John Davis hereby asserts his moral right to be identified as the author of this work in accordance with the Copyright, Designs and Patents Act, 1988.

ISBN 1902239 95 4

John Davis is an experienced primary school teacher who has written a number of books for teachers. He is author of *Maths and the Greeks* which is also published by Hopscotch Educational Publishing Ltd.

Introduction

The first settlers in Egypt moved into the fertile valley of the River Nile over 5,000 years ago to establish a civilisation that lasted from the period of the unification under the rule of Menes until the invasion of the Romans in 30BC.

During this time a succession of powerful pharaohs ran highly organised societies, encouraged the development of art, writing and trade, and embarked on elaborate building schemes that have astounded designers and architects with their grandeur and fascinated archaeologists with their treasures.

Mathematics, especially the ability to count, calculate and put the principles of geometry to practical use, played a key role in making these achievements possible. It is only now that experts are beginning to realise the importance of the Ancient Egyptians' influence on the mathematical thinking of later civilisations like the Greeks and the Romans.

The intention of this book is to allow busy teachers to link mathematics and history in a cross-curricular approach, saving them valuable time while also enriching a key core subject with an important foundation project area. There are also many opportunities to incorporate ICT, especially in Chapters 4 and 5.

Current documentation on mathematics emphasises the bonds between the subject and history, especially the Curriculum 2000 Maths Programme of Study for Key Stage 2, which states that 'pupils should be taught the knowledge, skills and understanding through using mathematics in their work in other subjects' (Breadth of Study 1h).

Ancient Egypt is included in the Curriculum 2000 history document as a world history study where it is stressed that children should consider 'significant places and individuals but also its distinctive contribution to history'. Further guidance is given in the QCA's Scheme of Work for History Unit 10: What can we find out about Ancient Egypt from what has survived?

This book is divided into five chapters – one for each of the main strands of the National Numeracy Strategy Framework.

- Each chapter opens with two **fact boxes** that are intended to provide important background information.

- This is followed by a range of **practical activities**, with helpful illustrations and diagrams, for children to carry out in the classroom working individually, with a partner or in a small group.

- **Teachers' notes** provide additional information, offer guidance and suggest extension tasks. Activities are fully referenced to NNSF teaching programmes for all the stages in Key Stage 2 from Year 3 through to Year 6.

- Because of the vital role played by mathematical language in the teaching and learning process, a **vocabulary box** containing key words is also included in each chapter.

- At the end of each chapter are nine carefully selected and **fully differentiated photocopiable tasks**. These are based on the themes described in the main text of the book and are for use in the classroom, although they would also be suitable for children to work on at home. Activity 1 is intended to be the easiest of the three sheets, Activity 2 more challenging and Activity 3 for higher-achieving children.

Numbers and the Number System

FACT BOX 1

A valuable legacy

Any society that could construct the pyramids and other large monuments, devise extensive irrigation systems, levy and collect taxes, carry out frequent censuses, run a well organised army and trade with other nations must have established a culture in which mathematics played a major role.

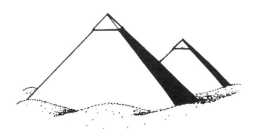

Yet for many years it was assumed that the arithmetic and geometry of the Ancient Egyptians was devised and practised purely for practical, everyday purposes and that it lacked the depth and quality of later civilisations, like the Greeks.

Since the discovery some 200 years ago of more reliable methods of translating hieroglyphic writing, however, scholars have been able to research ancient records to reveal a far more accurate picture of what was achieved in Egypt over 4,000 years ago.

By far the most significant breakthrough was the discovery in 1799 of a slab of basalt stone by the French army officer Jean-Francois Champollion during the construction of a fortress at Rosetta. This not only contained details written in Ancient Egyptian hieroglyphic and demotic script but also a convenient Greek translation. This discovery particularly has permitted intensive work to be carried out on the two most important mathematical documents from Ancient Egypt – the Rhind Papyrus, and the Golenishchev or Moscow Papyrus, which are discussed more fully in Fact box 1 on page 41.

Of the prominent mathematicians of Ancient Greece, Thales and Pythagoras are believed to have visited Egypt to broaden their knowledge. Thales became particularly interested in calculating the height of the pyramids while Pythagoras explored all situations where he thought he might discover something new. Later, they were among a number of other Greeks, including Proclus and Aristotle, who were keen to acknowledge the contribution the Egyptians had made to mathematics, especially for the stimulus they gave to those anxious to take that step beyond calculations into the realm of abstract thought.

FACT BOX 2

Picture writing

Ancient Egyptian mathematical knowledge has come to us from the Egyptians' use of hieroglyphics, or picture writing. There were over 700 hieroglyphic characters – a collection of symbols and pictures, some representing objects, others the sound of letters, or sometimes a combination of both these things. There were no symbols for vowels and this causes problems with modern translations.

Hieroglyphics were sometimes written and read upwards and downwards, sometimes from left to right, and often in the opposite direction. Today it is an accepted convention that many translations of Egyptian texts are reversed so that they read from left to right. Hieroglyphics were purposely kept complicated so that not many people would be able to use them. They were generally reserved for inscriptions on state monuments, temples and tombs and were also used on religious documents.

The Egyptian number system, like that adopted by many other ancient civilisations, was decimal in nature probably because of the total of ten fingers and thumbs found on both hands. Numbers up to and including nine could be written in single strokes (for example, six was | | | | | |) while there were picture symbols for the higher powers of ten.

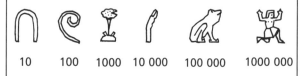

| 10 | 100 | 1000 | 10 000 | 100 000 | 1000 000 |

Recording numbers certainly involved more writing than using the system of digits that we have today. There are instances where a smaller number requires more characters than a larger one. For example, 1,968 requires 24 symbols while 30 000 can be written using only three.

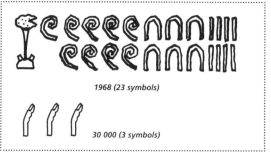

1968 (23 symbols)

30 000 (3 symbols)

Calculations also became more complicated and, as we shall see in Chapter 2, using ready-made tables often speeded up the process.

Numbers and the Number System

Picture Numbers

Details of the hieroglyphic symbols used for the numbers 1, 10, 100, 1,000, 10 000, 100 000 and 1 000 000 are given in Fact box 2 on page 4. Numbers were included in carved inscriptions and were also written in ink on papyrus. There is a good deal of speculation about what the symbols are intended to represent. Some suggestions merely name what the symbol is, for example 10 (heel bone), 100 (coiled rope), 1,000 (lotus flower), 10 000 (bent reed or finger),100 000 (fish, bird or frog) and 1 000 000 (surprised man). Others explain how the Egyptians arrived at that choice, for example 10 (the fetter used

to hold small groups of animals), 100 (a length of rope used to measure 100 cubits), 1,000 (group of flowers growing in a clump), 10 000 (bent reed or finger), 100 000 (tadpoles in a waterhole or a frog), 1 000 000 (a god looking up at the stars in the sky). Ask the children to suggest some theories of their own. They can practise writing these numbers on the photocopiable sheets: Egyptian Numbers 1, 2 and 3 on pages 12–14. Calculations involving the number system are given in Chapter 2.

Picture Numbers

The children will need plenty of practice in writing Ancient Egyptian numbers as the number system is based on drawn symbols and they will not be familiar with these. Find the best type of media for drawing the symbols quickly, for example a pencil, pen or felt-tipped pen. One bonus of the Egyptian method is that it uses the same base ten system as our own although the zero is notably absent. When the same symbol had to be repeated many times in the same number, such as the symbol for one in the number nine and the hundred in seven hundred, they were often grouped in batches of three or four, usually drawn vertically to save space (Figure 1). Discuss with the children the advantages and disadvantages of using a system like this.

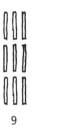
9

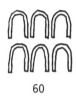
60

Figure 1

NNSF links: Year 3: *Read and write whole numbers to at least 1,000 in figures and words.* ***Year 4:*** *Read and write whole numbers to at least 10 000 in figures and words.* ***Year 5:*** *Read and write whole numbers in figures and words and know what each digit represents.* ***Year 6:*** *As Year 5.*

The Missing Zero

One reason the Egyptian number system eventually became impractical was the absence of a zero. In written work, particularly on papyri, a blank space was left instead, but this often led to confusion about the number being indicated or the calculation being carried out.

Give the children some tasks involving the zero in our current number system, emphasising its importance in the whole of our place value system. Stress the use of the word zero rather than 'nothing' as the 0 has value as a place or position holder separating columns of figures. Provide tasks on its significance in numbers like 108, 180, 1,008, 1,080, 1,800 and larger numbers like 180 000 and 1 800 000. Ask the children to write

down what numbers such as these would be in words or demonstrate how they appear on an abacus. Also ask the children to express them in what is known as expanded notation, for example 180 would be written as 100 + 80, 1,080 would be 1,000 + 80 and 180 000 would be 100 000 + 80 000.

Look at the effect the zero has when multiplying and dividing integers by 10 and by 100. Reinforce short methods of working here so that calculations can be carried out quickly and mentally. Multiplying by 10 and 100 will move digits to the left, for example 15 x 10 = 150 and 27 x 100 = 2,700. Dividing by 10 and 100 will move digits to the right, for example 160 ÷ 10 = 16 and 5,200 ÷ 100 = 52.

The zero was a much later invention and many attribute its common usage to the writings of the Italian mathematician Leonardo Fibonacci (1170–c1250), who stressed its importance in his book *Liber Abaci* or *The Book of Calculations*. Extend the children's investigations of the zero by asking the following questions. Can they prove that adding zero to any number keeps it unchanged? Is it the same when subtracting zero from any number? What is the answer when any number is multiplied by zero? Is it possible to divide a number by zero?

Discuss the use of zero in measurement. On weighing instruments and measuring tapes it means no weight or distance but on temperature scales it will have a valid reading, marking the point when positive numbers change to negative ones.

*NNSF links: **Year 4:** Multiply and divide any integer up to 1,000 by 10 and understand the effect. Begin to multiply by 100. **Year 5:** Multiply and divide any positive integer up to 10 000 by 10 or 100 and understand the effect. **Year 6:** Multiply and divide integers by 1,000 and explain the effect.*

The Abacus

There is evidence that the Ancient Egyptians, like the Babylonians, the Greeks and the Romans who came after them, used some form of abacus to help them with their practical counting activities. Abaci would have proved useful for recording and calculating the amount of food farmers were storing in granaries, making payments to soldiers in the army, and trading goods with other regions and countries, especially as money was not involved and transactions usually took place by bartering. The earliest form of abacus was probably a tray of sand divided into columns for ones, tens, hundreds and so on. Marks would have been made, or sometimes small stones or pebbles laid, to record the numbers being used. Encourage the children to make their own simple form of this abacus from the two suggestions in Figure 2.

Set the children some problems where they have to read off numbers shown on the abacus and vice versa (Figure 3).

Tasks using different forms of the abacus are given on photocopiable sheets: Abacus 1, 2, and 3 (pages 15–17).

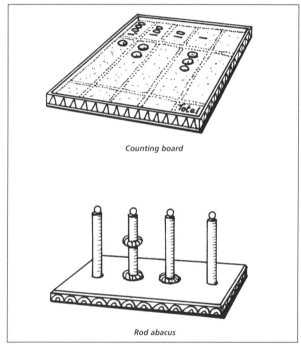

Counting board

Rod abacus

Figure 2

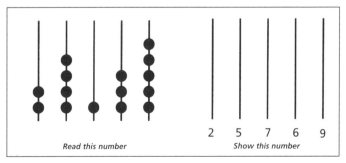

Read this number   2 5 7 6 9

Read this number   *Show this number*

Figure 3

The Abacus

The abacus is still used in some parts of the world today, especially China, Japan and the Middle East, and is the ancestor of the calculator and computer. Introduce the children to the abacus and reinforce their understanding of place value by using the counting board shown in Figure 2. Start by arranging counters on the board at random and asking the children to record the number that has been made.

Then challenge them in pairs to make as many different numbers as possible using only two counters, then three counters, then four. Ask them to record the numbers they make by using what is known as expanded notation. For example, 12 568 would be written as 10000 + 2000 + 500 + 60 + 8.

Show the children how to sink dowel rods into a wooden base to make a simple rod abacus (as shown in Figure 2). Use card rings or drilled wooden beads for the counting beads. Ask them to use the abacus to do addition and subtraction. Challenge the children to add or subtract 1, 10, 100 and 1,000 from any number given by dropping on or removing the necessary rings or beads. Remind the children that zero columns should be left blank but that the zero should be included in the correct position when the number is written down using digits.

NNSF links: **Year 3:** *Say the number that is 1, 10 or 100 more or less than any given two- or three-digit number.* **Year 4:** *Add/subtract 1, 10, 100 or 1,000 from any integer.* **Years 5 and 6:** *As Year 4.*

Rounding Off

Many large numbers are associated with the history of Ancient Egypt and it will help children with number recognition and place value if they have strategies to round off these numbers. For example, challenge the children to write, and then suitably round off, the estimated 2.3 million blocks of stone that make up the Great Pyramid at Giza. Then ask them to round off its dimensions of 228m in length at its base and 146m in height.

Other numbers to round off could include the following: the length of the country of Egypt (965km), the length of the River Nile (6670km), the birth of Tutankhamun (1336BC), the death of Hatshepsut (1488BC), the start of the Middle Kingdom Dynasty (c2040BC), the famous battle at Kadesh (1285BC) and the 1277 shabtis found in the tomb of Senkamanisken when there should have been only 401. Some of these numbers will also feature in Chapter 2.

Rounding Off

Explain to the children that rounding off numbers allows quick calculations to be carried out so that approximate answers can be obtained. Work on key vocabulary, particularly 'nearest', 'roughly', 'nearly' and 'approximately'. Reinforce the rules that apply to rounding off to the nearest 10, 100 and 1,000. The use of marked or blank number lines may prove useful. Explain that when rounding a number to the nearest 10, if the ones digit is less than halfway (1–4) it moves back to the previous 10. If it is exactly halfway or more (5–9) it moves on to the next 10. So, for example, 72 would be 70 and 158 would be 160. 50 would act as the halfway point for rounding to the nearest

100 and 500 for the nearest 1,000. Examples for the nearest 100 are: 759 to the nearest 100 would be 800 and 234 to the nearest 100 would be 200. For the nearest 1,000, 7,598 would be 8,000 and 16 374 would be 16 000.

NNSF links: **Year 3:** *Round any two-digit number to the nearest 10 and any three-digit number to the nearest 100.* **Year 4:** *Round any positive integer less than 1,000 to the nearest 10 or 100.* **Year 5:** *Round any integer up to 10 000 to the nearest 10, 100 or 1,000.* **Year 6:** *Consolidate rounding an integer to the nearest 10, 100 or 1,000.*

Square Numbers

Number problems found on the mathematical papyri left by the Ancient Egyptians show that they worked with the squares of numbers. Square roots, however, are far less common and although they are sometimes mentioned they are not calculated. It seems likely that scribes would have drawn up tables of square numbers so they could be found and read off quickly while calculations were in progress. The children should be familiar with all the square numbers up to 100, and beyond if possible (Figure 4).

Ask the children to look at the interesting pattern that is formed by the differences between square numbers. Encourage them to work in reverse order to see squaring a number and finding its square root as an inverse operation. For example, if 5^2 is 25 then the square root of 25 is 5. Calculators can be used to find the square of mixed numbers, such as $7\frac{1}{2}$, and the square root of numbers such as 30.

1^2	2^2	3^2	4^2	5^2	6^2	7^2	8^2	9^2	10^2
1 x 1	2 x 2	3 x 3	4 x 4	5 x 5	6 x 6	7 x 7	8 x 8	9 x 9	10 x 10
1	4	9	16	25	36	49	64	81	100

Figure 4

Square Numbers

Some children may need to draw the square numbers using squared paper or construct them on a pegboard in order to appreciate how this number pattern is created. Familiarise them with the use of index numbers when writing this particular number family, but do stress than 4^2 is 4 x 4 and not 4 x 2. The differences between square numbers increase by two and feature the odd numbers: 3, 5, 7, 9 and so on. Ask the children to investigate the way in which square numbers can be formed by adding consecutive numbers going up to the number you are squaring and then back down again, for example, 4 = 1 + 2 + 1, 9 = 1 + 2 + 3 + 2 + 1 and so on.

On a calculator the square of $7\frac{1}{2}$ would be calculated 7.5 x 7.5 = 56.25. To find the square root of a number such as 30, type in the number and then press the button showing the square root sign ($\sqrt{}$). The answer should appear as 5.48 to two decimal places.

*NNSF links: **Year 3:** Describe and extend number sequences. **Year 4:** Recognise and extend number sequences. **Year 5:** Know squares of numbers to at least 10 x 10. **Year 6:** Recognise squares of numbers to at least 12 x 12.*

Algebra

Although the Ancient Egyptians did not work with the concept of algebra as such, there are examples in the Rhind Papyrus where they considered problems involving missing numbers. They were often written out in words with the term 'heap' being used to represent an unknown number. The scribe responsible for compiling this document is particularly fond of showing general methods of finding a solution for certain types of questions. Formal algebra does not really begin until Key Stage 3 but important preparation work needs to be done in Key Stage 2.

First, focus activities on solving equations, such as 27 + ☐ = 53 and ☐ x 24 = 192. Investigate problems in which children have a choice so they appreciate the unknown may be a variable and not a fixed number, for example ☐ + ∆ = 54 and 7 x ☐ = ∆. Find the missing number in inverse operations, for example, if 28 + 53 = 81, 81 – 28 = ☐. Then ask the children to identify missing numbers in sequences, such as 56, 51, 46, ☐, 36, 31. Use signs and symbols to express relationship and formula for calculations, for example, c (cost) = n (number) x p (price), or a (area) of a rectangle = l (length) x w (width). Work here is supported and extended by the 'think of a number' activities in Chapter 3 (page 42).

During these activities, emphasise to the children the importance of the equals sign in equations as it acts as a balance between the two sides of the statement. Consolidate the work suggested with the use of letter symbols standing for missing numbers. But remind the children that in algebra when a number and a letter stand immediately next to each other it means multiply, for example $5b = 5 \times b$. Also that when numbers move from one side of an equation to the other, they change their sign – add becomes subtract and vice versa. For example, given $6c + 14 = 32$ then $6c = 32 - 14$, $6c = 18$ and $c = 3$.

*NNSF links: **Year 3:** Solve mathematical problems or puzzles, recognise simple patterns and relationships. Explain methods and reasoning. **Years 4, 5 and 6:** As for Year 3.*

Fractions

The Egyptians were certainly one of the first civilisations to work with the concept of a fraction, but they seem to have made life doubly difficult for themselves. Only unit fractions were permitted – that is, fractions with a numerator of one. These are sometimes called 'aliquot' fractions. Documents suggest that it was not permitted to repeat a fraction when making up another fractional amount. The fewest number of fractions had to be used and the largest usually came first. The only exception to the unit fraction rule appears to be two-thirds, which is used frequently. However, there is evidence of three-quarters appearing in some places although it was usually written as $\frac{1}{2} + \frac{1}{4}$. Set the children tasks where they are restricted to using unit fractions only – for example, finding five-sixths, three-fifths and five-eighths (Figure 5).

1															

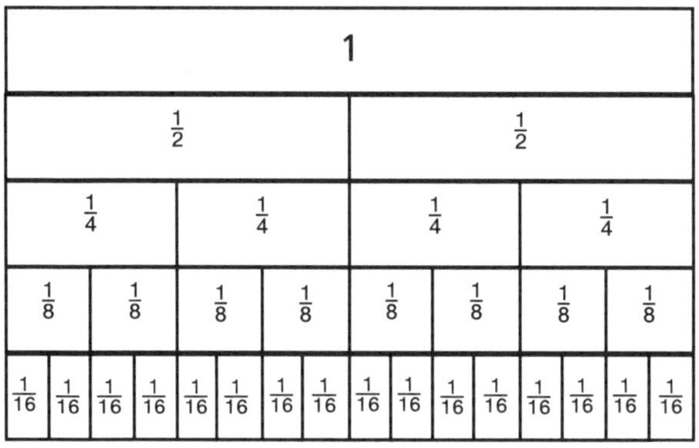

Figure 6

Use number lines for locating fractions (Figure 7), compare common and decimal fractions, and begin to relate fractions to the process of division (Figure 8).

$$\frac{5}{6} = \frac{1}{3} + \frac{1}{3} + \frac{1}{6}$$

$$\frac{3}{5} = \frac{1}{5} + \frac{1}{5} + \frac{1}{5}$$

$$\frac{5}{8} = \frac{1}{4} + \frac{1}{4} + \frac{1}{8}$$

Figure 5

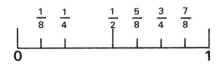

Figure 7

Look at key vocabulary such as 'numerator', 'denominator', 'mixed number', 'improper fraction', 'equivalent fraction' and 'cancelling down' by finding the 'highest common factor'.

Work with fraction boards to help children find out more about equivalence (Figure 6).

$$\tfrac{1}{2} \text{ of } 30 = 30 \div 2$$

$$\tfrac{2}{3} \text{ of } 27 = 27 \div 3 \times 2$$

Figure 8

Problems using fractions are given on photocopiable sheets: Fractions 1, 2 and 3 (pages 18–20).

Children need to appreciate that fractions are a part of a whole number or amount. In the simple fraction $\frac{3}{4}$ the 4 shows the fraction family and is called the denominator and the 3 shows the number of parts and is called the numerator. An equivalent fraction is where the same value is expressed in a different form, for example one half is the same as four-eighths and five-tenths. Decimal fractions are another method of expressing a common fraction, so $\frac{1}{4}$ = 0.25. Mixed numbers are a mixture of whole numbers and fractions, for example $3\frac{1}{2}$, and improper fractions occur when the numerator is larger than the denominator.

Division and fractions are closely related when finding fractional amounts. A quarter of 12, for example, is the same as 12 ÷ 4 = 3. To find $\frac{3}{4}$ of a number, divide by 4 and then multiply by 3 – for example, $\frac{3}{4}$ of 20 = 20 ÷ 4 = 5, then 5 x 3 = 15. With all problem-solving activities involving fractions, encourage the children to think about the general rules and strategies involved, not just finding the answer.

NNSF links: Year 3: Recognise unit fractions. Begin to recognise simple fractions that are several parts of a whole. Begin to recognise equivalent fractions. Year 4: Use fraction notation. Order simple fractions. Begin to relate fractions to division. Year 5: Change an improper fraction to a mixed number. Recognise when two simple fractions are equivalent. Relate fractions to division. Year 6: Recognise relationships between fractions. Reduce a fraction to its simplest terms by cancelling down. Use a fraction as an 'operator' to find fractions, for example five-sixths of 42.

Ratio and Proportion

As designers and builders, the Egyptians believed that large constructions were easier to build and more pleasing on the eye once completed if their dimensions were kept in proportion. They referred to it as the 'sacred ratio' and used it on the building of the Great Pyramid at Giza. Here the ratio of the height of a face to half of the base is 1.681: 1. There is also evidence in the Rhind Papyrus that the Egyptians used ratios to make sure the pyramids faced in the right direction.

Furthermore, they appear to have had a table of ratios that pyramid builders could use to ensure that all four triangular faces would slope at the correct angle and meet at a single point. Other studies of their technology skills have shown that the ratio between the length of a granite obelisk and the width of its base could not be more than between 10 or 11 without the risk that it would fracture during the course of erection.

Start with practical construction problems involving proportion by asking the children to make towers like the obelisk. If one in every three stones is black, how many black stones will there be in a column twelve stones high? (Figure 9)

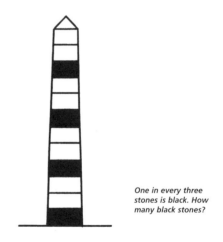

One in every three stones is black. How many black stones?

Figure 9

Then move on to more abstract problems set in context. If there are two men for every three women living in a village on the banks of the River Nile and there are a total of 100 villagers altogether, how many women are there? Try sharing activities. If the baker has 16 loaves and gives one loaf to A for every three loaves he gives to B, how many do they each receive?

Ratio and Proportion

Ratios are best used to compare different amounts or quantities. They are usually written as numbers separated by a colon, for example 1:3. They are closely linked to fractions but should not be confused with them. For example, the fraction $\frac{3}{4}$ refers to three parts of a whole divided into four parts while the ratio 3:4 means three parts and four parts of a whole divided into seven parts.

Ratios can have more than two quantities, especially in the ingredients of recipes where the amounts can be varied depending on the numbers involved without changing the taste or the texture.

Key phrases in these activities will include 'in every', 'for every' and 'to every'. In the practical examples given on the previous page there would be four black stones in the obelisk. For the villagers problem, the solution would be 2:3 = 5. 100 ÷ 5 = 20, so 20 x 2 = 40 men and 20 x 3 = 60 women. Concerning the baker and loaves, 1 + 3 = 4, 16 ÷ 4 = 4, so A gets 4 and B gets 12.

*NNSF links: **Year 4:** Begin to use ideas of simple proportion.*
__Year 5:__ Solve simple problems using ideas of ratio and proportion.
__Year 6:__ Solve simple problems involving ratio and proportion.

Vocabulary Box

abacus	equivalent fraction	ratio
algebra	expanded notation	Rhind Mathematical Papyrus
aliquot fraction	formula	rounding off
approximate	hieroglyphics	scribe
base ten system	highest common factor	square number
cancel down	improper fraction	square root
consecutive number	index number	symbol
decimal number	inverse operation	unit fraction
denominator	numerator	zero
digit	obelisk	
dimensions	papyrus	
dynasty	proportion	

Picture Signs

○ Scribes in Ancient Egypt used the picture signs shown in the box below to write numbers and carry out calculations.

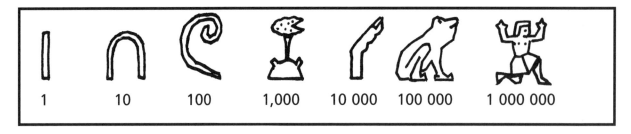

○ These are some of the picture signs a scribe has collected in his work. What numbers do they show?

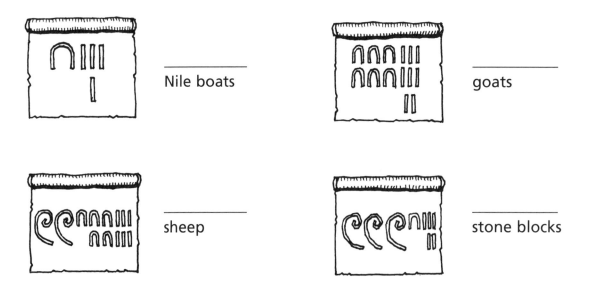

Nile boats _____

goats _____

sheep _____

stone blocks _____

○ Now write down these numbers on the scrolls of papyrus.

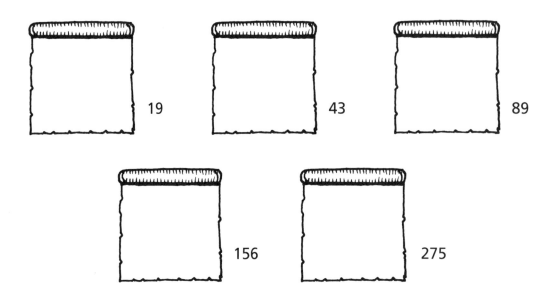

19

43

89

156

275

Scribe School

○ Spet has just started studying at a special school for trainee scribes.

○ His teacher has asked him to write the following numbers neatly on a sheet of papyrus. Notice that picture signs, shown in the box on the right, are usually written down in groups of three.

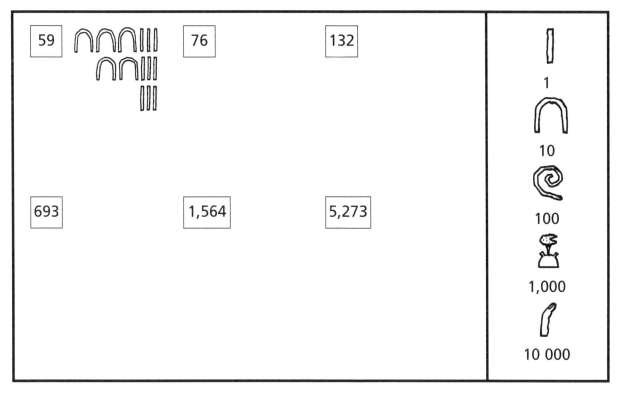

○ Here are some numbers that Spet wrote yesterday. Translate them into our number system. Which number system do you think is best? Give reasons for your answer.

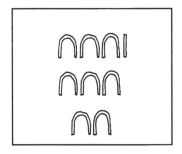

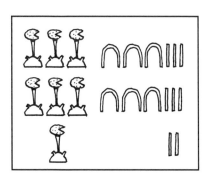

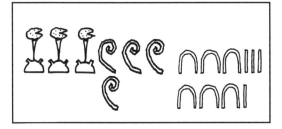

Pharaoh's Census

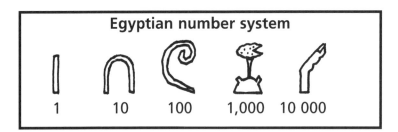

Egyptian number system

1	10	100	1,000	10 000

○ Pharaoh has ordered that a census be carried out in towns and villages along the banks of the River Nile.

○ These are the numbers of people the scribe Sofer has counted, but how did he write them in Egyptian picture signs or hieroglyphics (shown in the box above)? Work on a separate piece of paper and remember to write the totals as well.

	Women	Men	Children	Total
• Village 1	54	23	19	
• Village 2	27	45	36	
• Town 1	193	209	114	
• Town 2	1564	2147	1956	

○ The people in other places have also been counted by Sofer. These are his results. This time translate the picture signs back into our own number system to find out how many people live in each place. Again, you will need to calculate the totals.

	Women	Men	Children	Total
• Village 3	∩∩∩ ∩∩ |||	∩∩∩ ∩∩∩ ||| |||	∩∩ ||| ||| ||	
• Village 4	ℓℓℓ ℓℓℓ ∩∩		ℓℓℓ ℓℓ ∩∩∩ ∩∩∩ |||	ℓℓℓ ℓℓℓ ℓ ∩ ||| ||	

Loose Pebbles

○ The first kind of abacus used in Egypt was probably drawn in the sand and used small stones or pebbles.

○ Find a small rectangular tray or board and cover it with a layer of dry, clean sand about 2cm deep. Use two fingers held together to make straight grooves in the sand. This will make columns for 1, 10, 100 and 1,000.

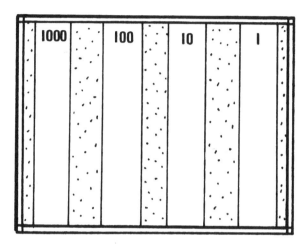

○ Place smooth stones or pebbles in the grooves to show numbers. You could use counters. The abacus below shows 3,521.

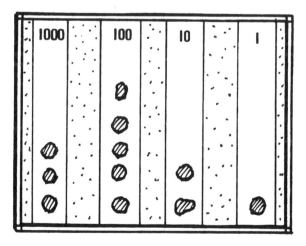

○ Show these numbers on your abacus: 45, 92, 153, 275, 1,364, 4,592, 5,107 and 8,039.

○ Make some numbers for your friend to name. Then ask them to make some numbers for you.

Counting Board

○ People who lived in ancient times, like the Egyptians, made abaci to help them with their counting and calculations.

○ Make a simple abacus counting board that is big enough to deal with five-digit numbers. You will need some thick cardboard and coloured counters.

○ This is what the counting board should look like. It is displaying the number 7,254.

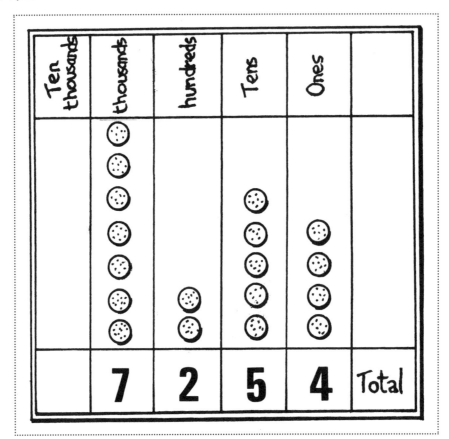

○ On your counting board, make these numbers and ask a friend to say them out loud to you: 43, 78, 107, 563, 729, 924, 1,027, 1,264, 3,598 and 31 205.

○ Round off 43 and 78 to the nearest 10.

○ Round off 107, 563, 729 and 924 to the nearest 10 and the nearest 100.

○ Round off 1,027, 1,264, 3,598 and 31 205 to the nearest 10, 100 and 1,000.

○ Ask a friend to make some numbers for you to read off on the counting board and then round them off in the same way as before.

Spare the Rod

○ The Ancient Egyptians used an abacus to help them with their counting and calculating.

○ Carry out some number work of your own by making a rod abacus from pieces of wood. Ask a friend to help you.

○ To make a rod abacus like the one shown below, you will need a wooden baseboard, thin dowel rods, paper and sticky tape for labelling and wooden beads or thick cardboard rings. You will also need a saw, a drill and some strong wood glue. Ask an adult to help you.

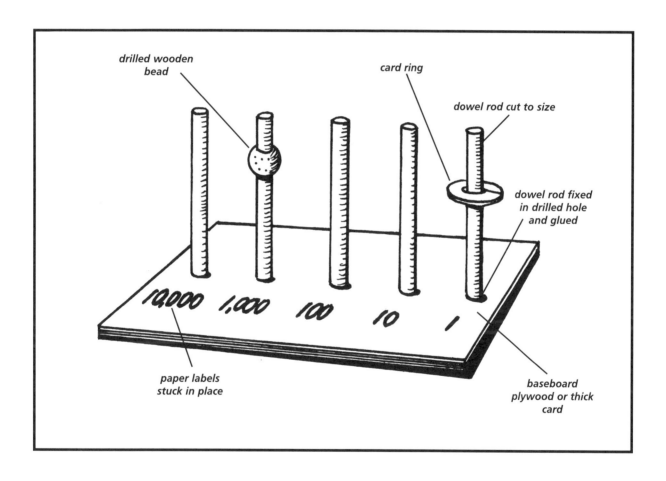

○ This abacus can show five-digit numbers up to 99 999 but you can make yours show 100 000 or even 1 000 000 if you wish. Just include extra rods.

○ Once your abacus is ready, show some numbers for your friend to identify. Then swap over and let them make up some numbers for you. Find the largest and smallest number you have both made. Take some of the numbers you or your friend have made and order them, sometimes going from smallest to largest and sometimes in the reverse order.

Round Loaves

○ Below are the round loaves that Wary the baker makes in Ancient Egypt.

○ He has to make sure his customers get their correct share of the loaf when he pays them for his materials like wheat and salt.

○ Colour in the correct fraction so that he does not make a mistake when he cuts up the loaf.

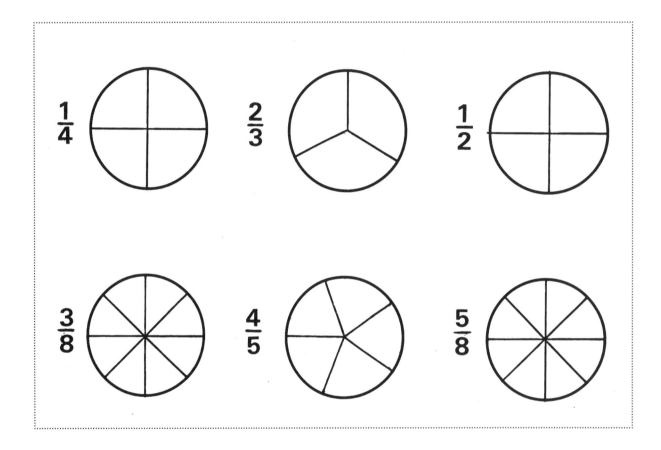

○ Work out these other fraction calculations for Wary by using division.
Remember $\frac{1}{2}$ of 12 is the same as 12 ÷ 2.

$\frac{1}{3}$ of 12 loaves $\frac{1}{5}$ of 45 grapes

$\frac{1}{2}$ of 24 cakes $\frac{1}{10}$ of 90 figs

$\frac{1}{4}$ of 32 dates $\frac{2}{3}$ of 15 eggs

All In Order

○ Here are some loaves of bread that Wary has been baking in his oven in Ancient Egypt.

○ He has divided them up into fractions to share out among his customers.

○ Put each row of loaves in order of size, starting with the smallest fraction. You may need to put some fractions into the same family to help you sort them out. Write the fractions in order next to the loaves.

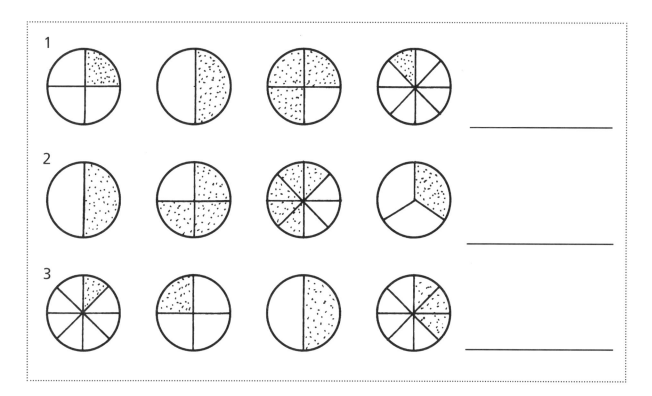

1

2

3

○ Find these amounts that Wary also needs to work out for his customers. Remember $\frac{1}{4}$ of 20 is 20 ÷ 4 and $\frac{3}{4}$ of 12 is 12 ÷ 4 x 3.

$\frac{1}{5}$ of 35 cakes $\frac{3}{8}$ of 64 jars of honey

$\frac{2}{3}$ of 36 loaves $\frac{9}{10}$ of 120 figs

$\frac{3}{4}$ of 60 grapes $\frac{5}{9}$ of 117 dates

Just The One

○ The Ancient Egyptian scribes always tried to work in unit fractions – that is, fractions that have 1 as the numerator – for example, $\frac{1}{5}$. These are also called aliquot fractions.

○ When working with fractions, they always tried to use the least number of unit fractions and they always wrote the largest one first.
Here is an example: $\frac{3}{4} = \frac{1}{2} + \frac{1}{4}$

○ Make up these fractions using only unit fractions and follow the rules given above. Some of them may produce more than one solution. When you have done this, try out some fractions of your own in the same way in the box.

$\frac{1}{2}$ _____

$\frac{3}{8}$ _____

$\frac{2}{3}$ _____

$\frac{5}{6}$ _____

$\frac{3}{10}$ _____

$\frac{4}{7}$ _____

○ One exception to these rules that scribes often used was the fraction $\frac{2}{3}$.
Help the scribe to find two-thirds of these numbers.

$\frac{2}{3}$ of 27

$\frac{2}{3}$ of 156

$\frac{2}{3}$ of 42

$\frac{2}{3}$ of 366

$\frac{2}{3}$ of 60

$\frac{2}{3}$ of 5,442

Calculations

F A C T

1

B O X

The education system

One scribe in Ancient Egypt had no doubt of the importance of a good education when he stressed on his papyrus, 'Writing, for one who knows how, is more profitable than all other professions. See I am instructing you … so that you may become one who is trusted by the king.'

However, most children from ordinary families probably did not get the chance to go to school and that is why so few people were able to read and write. They usually followed in the footsteps of parents by becoming farmers, craft workers or labourers. Education was restricted mainly to boys with wealthy parents and often took place in large temples and palaces where space was set aside for daily instruction. Alternatively, private tutors visited homes to teach.

Most girls did not attend school. Few could read and write and at home they were instructed in the skills of cooking and housekeeping and also learned about music and dancing. There is evidence though, on tomb paintings, to suggest that a small number of girls received the same education as boys and went on to qualify as scribes.

Lessons were long and tedious. With over 700 hieroglyphic signs to be mastered, sessions were spent memorising symbols, copying text and writing from dictation. Pupils must have found it hard to concentrate as they saw and heard their friends playing outside in the sunshine. Early attempts at writing were tried on loose pieces of stone called 'ostraca'. Only after some skill had been acquired were pupils allowed to graduate to reed pens and papyrus.

Schooling usually took place between the ages of nine and 12, although boys whose ambition it was to become scribes often continued until they were 16. As boys became older, they were taught mathematics along with history and geography, and studied problems related to building, surveying and engineering. Discipline was harsh. Teachers followed the maxim, 'A boy's ears are on his back. He listens when he is beaten.'

Greek scholars who visited Egypt and saw the type of instruction being given were impressed. They took aspects of this teaching and used them in their own education system. Later, the philosopher Plato was to write, 'Freeborn children should learn as much of these things as the throngs of young in Egypt do with their alphabet. As regards arithmetic, lessons have been devised there for absolute beginners based on enjoyment and games.'

F A C T

2

B O X

The scribes

As mathematicians, writers, teachers and detailed recorders of the daily life of Ancient Egypt, scribes formed an important part of the ruling elite. They ranked equal in position with noblemen and were almost on a par with viziers and priests. Top jobs included head temple scribe, keeper of tax returns and government reports, chief recorder at the law courts, personal tutor to the wealthy, and head librarian. Others worked out the rations needed for the army, maintained supplies of building materials, charted numbers in herds of cattle, made records of the grain harvest and kept registers of trade both within Egypt and other neighbouring countries. Since everything had to be calculated, written down and accounted for, Egypt could not survive without them. Scribes organised and ran the country like the forerunners of today's civil service.

Most of the recording carried out by the scribes was done on papyrus. This was a form of paper made from thin strips of papyrus reed of which there was a plentiful supply in Egypt growing along the banks of the River Nile. The strips were placed together in a criss-cross pattern and then hammered with a mallet to make a single sheet. One of the main advantages of papyrus was that it could be rolled up and easily stored. It is from these rolls that we know a great deal about life in Ancient Egypt.

Scribes usually carried a wooden palette that contained their writing pens and ink supplies. The palette needed to be portable, as scribes were often required to travel during the course of their work. They wrote with long reed pens using blocks of ink that were mixed with water before use. Inks were coloured with soot, charcoal or coloured minerals such as ochre. Black ink was used for ordinary writing while titles and headings were often written in red.

Scribes had their own hieroglyphic sign. It showed two wells of ink, a reed penholder and a water pot complete with shoulder strap for carrying the equipment. Together the symbols make up the Egyptian word for a qualified scribe.

With a long, rigorous and difficult training, the drop-out rate at scribe school seems to have been high. Papyri have been found in which senior scribes rebuke young colleagues for neglecting their studies and in some cases recommend corporal punishment. They encourage them to keep at their work and highlight that the advantages of gaining qualifications is that it will give them a position in society that will make it all worthwhile.

Calculations

Finger Calculating

Like many children in school these days, ancient peoples like the Egyptians would have relied on simple finger calculating when there were no facilities to write numbers down or use equipment such as an abacus. The single stroke that the Egyptians used for 1 is easily identified with an extended single finger and the symbols used for other members of the base ten families can also be illustrated by using the fingers and hands.

Try out some practical demonstrations with the children first. For 10, use the rounded arch between the thumb and index finger (Figure 1) and for the coiled rope, 100, a hand arched over (Figure 2).

For the larger numbers from 1,000 upward, try the suggestions made in Figure 3. When the children are familiar with these, try out some finger-based activities involving number identification and some simple calculation of addition and subtraction.

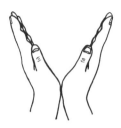

two hands touching

1,000

a bent index finger

10 000

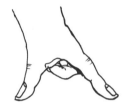

Figure 1

clenched fist like frog

100 000

arms/hands raised

1 000 000

Figure 2

Figure 3

Finger Calculating

Ask the children to explain the way in which they use their fingers in order to carry out or check simple calculations. Then extend the tasks by using several modern examples.

Fingers, for example, are often a great help in calculating the nine times table. Both hands are held up in front and the thumbs and fingers numbered from one to ten from left to right. To calculate 2 x 9, bend down the second finger. The finger to the left of the bent finger shows the tens and those on the right the units or ones. The answer would be 18 (see diagram below).

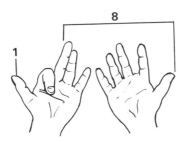

Try out the binary system – the counting system common to computers that only uses the numerals 0 and 1. Number the fingers according to the powers of two as shown.

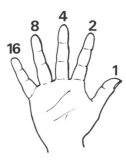

In the binary system, 3 is 11 because it is made up of one 2 and one 1. These are the fingers being shown. 10 is 1010 because it is made up of one 8, no 4's, one 2 and no 1's. The binary system uses the numbers 1, 2, 4, 8, 16 and so on because these are the powers of 2, that is $2^0 = 1$, $2^1 = 2$, $2^2 = 4$, $2^3 = 8$, $2^4 = 16$ and so on.

The number three should be shown by the raised thumb and index finger:

11 = 3

Four should be shown by just the second finger, and ten by the raised eight and two fingers:

1010 = 10

Children may be interested in a rather gruesome footnote. One method apparently used by the Egyptians to calculate the number of soldiers who had died in battle was to journey around the battlefield cutting a hand off of each of the bodies. The hands were then counted up. They could then be certain that no one had been missed or some bodies counted twice.

NNSF links: **Year 3:** *Choose and use appropriate operations to solve word problems.* **Year 4:** *As Year 3.* **Year 5:** *Choose and use appropriate number operations to solve problems and appropriate ways of calculating.* **Year 6:** *As Year 5.*

Using Signs

In the documents of Ancient Egypt, it is usually clear what type of arithmetical calculation is being carried out from information given. But there are occasions when picture signs are used especially to denote addition and subtraction. One contemporary writer, stressing their importance, described signs and symbols as 'directions for knowing all dark things'. In the Rhind Papyrus, for example, a pair of legs walking forward means add and a pair of legs walking backwards (Figure 4), or sometimes a flight of arrows, represents subtraction. Try the 'walking signs' out in the calculations suggested later in this chapter.

Since multiplication and division was carried out largely through repeated addition or repeated subtraction, signs for these operations appear not to have been used.

Set the children some activities to reinforce the correct use in our calculations today of the four main operation signs and the equals sign. Also concentrate on signs with which the children are less familiar. Use the signs < and > in a range of number statements and calculations involving whole numbers (175 > 157), fractions ($\frac{1}{4}$ < $\frac{3}{4}$), and decimals (1.12 > 0.99).

Also work on how the signs + and − are used to indicate positive and negative numbers, particularly in a practical context such as temperature. The children should be able to place numbers on a positive/negative number line and count up and down it, order positive and negative numbers and calculate the differences between them (Figure 5).

legs forward   legs in opposite direction

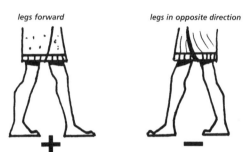

Figure 4

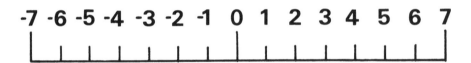

Figure 5

Using Signs

Even older children with more experience often have difficulty using the signs < and >. Reinforce that the open part of sign always goes towards the larger number but the reading of the statement always goes from left to right. So the statement 152 > 115 would read 152 is bigger than 115 and the statement 350 < 375 would read 350 is smaller than 375.

In the same way, plenty of practice is needed so that the children appreciate that there is a number line below zero where negative numbers are found. Many children find the need to work with an actual number line so that they can use a pencil to move physically along the line when counting moves up or down. Remember that when finding differences the general rule is that same signs indicate subtraction while different signs imply addition. For example −7 to −2 = 5 and +3 to +10 = 7 while −1 to +5 = 6 and +10 to −3 = 13.

NNSF links: Years 3 and 4: Use symbols correctly including less than (<), greater than (>) and equals (=). Recognise negative numbers in context. Years 5 and 6: Use the vocabulary of comparing and ordering numbers including symbols such as <, > and =. Order a given set of positive and negative integers. Find the difference between positive and negative integers.

Adding and Subtracting

Despite the fact that calculations involving addition and subtraction must have been carried out daily by skilled scribes, there is little evidence in papyri to show the methods that were used. Perhaps it was thought that the processes were so obvious and mundane it was not worth recording them. It has been suggested that these operations were carried out and checked elsewhere and that the answers were filled in later. Another theory is that since errors in this type of calculation are rare, tables for addition and subtraction may have existed from which solutions could just be read off.

Encourage the children to make their own addition square tables that can be used to launch number investigations. One possibility is shown in Figure 6.

+	1	2	3	4	⟶	9
1						
2						
3						
4						
↓						
9						

Figure 6

Using the completed square table, ask the children to look for interesting number patterns. They should then mark off small squares and rectangles and add the numbers found in opposite corners (Figure 7).

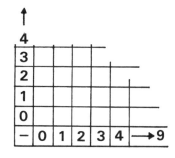

2	3	4
3	4	5
4	5	6

$2 + 6 = 8$

$4 + 4 = 8$

4	5	6	7
5	6	7	8
6	7	8	9

$4 + 9 = 13$

$7 + 6 = 13$

Figure 7

Challenge the children to add the numbers along the legs of a 3 x 3 cross and find the relationship between this total and the number at the centre of the cross. Try the same activity with a 5 x 5 cross.

Use the same square for subtraction, always taking the smaller number away from the larger one (Figure 8).

↑						
4						
3						
2						
1						
0						
−	0	1	2	3	4	⟶ 9

Figure 8

What patterns are made this time? Compare the subtraction square with the addition square.

Adding and Subtracting

It will speed up the process and help the children to focus immediately on the investigation aspects if copies of completed squares are provided. In the addition square, opposite corners of the squares or rectangles will add up to the same total. In a 3 x 3 square, the total of each 'leg' of the cross, horizontal or vertical, should be the same as the middle number trebled. In the 5 x 5 crosses, the procedure will be the same only this time the middle number will need to be multiplied by five. For extension work, encourage the children to investigate other addition squares using different numbers in the outside edge of the grids. Also look at the historical importance of using an addition grid such as a 'ready reckoner', especially when items were being sold at the same price – for example, 1 spade costs £10.75; 2 spades cost £21.50; 3 spades cost £32.25.

NNSF links: Year 3: Extend understanding of the operations of addition and subtraction. Year 4: Consolidate understanding of the relationship between + and −. Years 5 and 6: As for Year 4.

Multiplication and Division

When the Egyptian scribe needed to multiply two numbers, all he needed was the ability to double numbers and then carry out some addition. If, to take a simple example, he wanted to multiply 13 and 17 he put 1 on the left and the larger of the two numbers, 17, on the right. He doubled both numbers until the number on the left was more than half of the smaller number. Check markers were placed beside the numbers on the left that added up to 13. The corresponding numbers on the right were then totalled up to find the answer (Figure 9).

Egyptian multiplication: 13 x 17

1✓	17✓
2	34
4✓	68✓
8✓	136✓
——	——
13	221

Figure 9

Sometimes a method including direct multiplication by 10 was involved in order to speed up the operation (Figure 10).

The process of division was closely linked to this. If the scribe wanted to divide 216 by 9, he did not think in terms of dividing 9 into 216 but in terms of by what he must multiply 9 to get 216. He would keep doubling both columns of numbers until the next number on the right would be well past 216. Check marks were placed on the right against numbers that totalled 216 and the numbers opposite these on the left would provide him with the answer (Figure 11).

Egyptian multiplication x 10
quick method: 14 x 15

1	15
10✓	150✓
2	30
4✓	60✓
——	——
14	210

Figure 10

In this quick method, the 10 and 140 (being the numbers 14 and 15 times 10) are put second because this takes a large part out of the 14 straight away.

Egyptian division: 216 ÷ 9

1	9
2	18
4	36
8✓	72✓
16✓	144✓
——	——
24	216

Figure 11

The opportunity for children to try out some of these calculation methods in context is provided on the photocopiable sheets: Multiplication and division 1, 2 and 3 (pages 32–34).

Multiplication and Division

Take the opportunity with this method of multiplying to reinforce the children's doubling skills and also to link them with halving, as the two processes go so closely together. Work particularly on doubling and halving using the partition method – for example, double 76 is double 70 + double 6 = 140 + 12 = 152, or half of 98 is a half of 90 and a half of 8 = 45 + 4 = 49. Doubling can also help children with some of the multiplication tables – for example, x 6 is x 3 doubled and x 4 is a number doubled and then doubled again. Because of the close links between multiplication and division in the method used above, also work on the use of the inverse operation and how it can be used to check calculations. Make comparisons between the Egyptian method of multiplication and the system used later by the Greeks where halving came more into operation. What are the advantages and disadvantages of both methods?

NNSF links: Year 3: Understand multiplication as repeated addition. Year 4: Extend understanding of the operations of x and ÷ and their relationship to each other. Year 5: Understand the effect of and relationship between the four operations and the principles of the arithmetic laws as they apply to multiplication. Year 6: Understand the relationships between the four operations and the principles of the arithmetic laws.

Big Numbers

Link the following activities with the rounding off activities suggested on page 7.

Use large numbers connected with the history of Ancient Egypt for calculation work aimed at sharpening mental skills. For example, ask the children to use counting on methods to find out the length of Tutankhamun's reign, 1336BC to 1327BC. Alternatively, ask them to find the difference between larger numbers by using number facts and place value – for example, the reign of the longest serving pharoah Pepy II 2246BC to 2152BC and the time span of the Middle Kingdom c2040BC to 1640BC.

Challenge the children to compare the height of the Great Pyramid (146m) and other tall buildings, like the Statue of Liberty (92m), and to calculate the perimeter of the Great Pyramid that measures 230m on each of its four sides.

Encourage the children to suggest which calculation methods are best used to find the composition of the Egyptian army in the time of the New Kingdom. Each of the four regiments, named after a god, had 20 companies each. There were 200 infantry and 25 two-man chariots in each company. How many foot soldiers were there? How many charioteers? How many soldiers was this altogether?

Big Numbers

A variety of strategies could be used to work out these calculations, but the following are among the most widely used.

Find differences between smaller numbers by counting on from the smaller to the larger – for example,1327BC to 1336BC would be nine years. With larger differences, work through convenient multiples of ten and a hundred – for example, Pepy's reign 2246BC to 2152BC would be 2246 to 2240 (6 years), 2240 to 2200 (40 years), 2200 to 2160 (40 years) and 2160 to 2152 (8 years). This makes a total of 94 years altogether giving him the title of the longest reigning monarch in the history of the world.

Add up three-digit numbers by partitioning and dealing with the most significant digits first – for example, the perimeter of the four-sided Great Pyramid would be 200 + 200 + 200 + 200 = 800m and 30 + 30 + 30 + 30 = 120m giving 800 + 120 = 920m.

A range of methods could be used to find the fighting strength of the Egyptian army. Several should be tried in order to check out results. The children should find there are 16 000 infantry (80 companies x 200 men) and 4,000 charioteers (80 companies x 50 men). This makes a total of 20 000 in the army altogether.

NNSF links: Year 3: Find small differences by counting up from the smaller to the larger number. Year 4: Use known number facts and place value to subtract mentally. Year 5: Partition into H, T, U, adding the most significant digits first. Year 6: Check with an equivalent calculation.

Pyramid Numbers

Further work on children's addition skills can be carried out by utilising the triangular shape provided by the face of a pyramid and the way it was constructed using rows of stones. Adding two adjacent numbers and entering their total on the stone immediately above forms pyramid numbers. The number of stones decrease by one each time as you move towards the apex of the triangular shape. An example of this is given in Figure 12.

As the children become more adept, leave blank stones in random positions and eventually provide empty pyramids so that they can originate their own number structure. Set target numbers for them to achieve by the time they reach the top stone. Can they choose numbers to make the top number more than 50, for example, or less than 25, more than 80 or exactly 46?

Ideas for the children to try out at different levels are given on photocopiable sheets: Pyramid Numbers 1, 2 and 3 (pages 35–37).

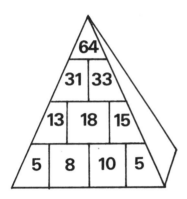

Figure 12

Pyramid Numbers

Suggest that the children try adding fractions or decimal numbers instead of integers in the pyramids. They could also investigate the sequence known as triangular numbers. This pattern runs 1, 3, 6, 10, 15, 21, and so on. The children can form the sequence practically using coins, counters or inter-locking cubes (see the diagram below).

Counters

```
    O       8       8        8
           O O     8 8      8 8 8
                  O O O    O O O O
    1       3       6        10
```

Cubes

```
    1       3       6        10
```

By looking at the differences between the numbers, ask the children to predict how it will continue. Then challenge them to investigate how triangular numbers can be made by totalling up consecutive numbers – for example, 1 + 2 = 3, 1 + 2 + 3 = 6, 1 + 2 + 3 + 4 = 10.

There are other points of interest. The sum of two consecutive triangular numbers appear to produce a square number – for example, 1 + 3 = 4 and 10 + 15 = 25. Try some others. Tell the children about the work carried out on numbers in the shape of a triangle by the French mathematician Blaise Pascal, called Pascal's Triangle. In this case, adjacent numbers are added to form the numbers that come below them. The examination of this triangle can lead to a range of other important number investigations.

NNSF links: Year 3: Solve mathematical problems and or puzzles. Year 4: Explain methods and reasoning about numbers orally and in writing. Years 5 and 6: Same as Year 4.

Dice Games

Cubed dice with markings very similar to those we still use today have been found in tombs in Egypt that date back to 2000BC. Some evidence suggests that they might even have been used in religious ceremonies. Early peoples, like the Egyptians, tended to make dice from plum and peach stones, bone, horn, pebbles, pottery or shells while later much more ornate ones were produced from bronze, ivory, agate and onyx. Dice were either rolled from the hand or from a dice cup to land on numbers at random. It was one of the earliest forms of gambling. Right from the start, apparently, cheats attempted to prosper by trying to stack the odds in their favour. Initially, cubes were shaved down on one or more sides so that they tended to settle on the larger surfaces. When these changes became detectable, small weights were attached below the surface of some faces to influence how the dice would roll.

With the children, look at problems caused by the way dice faces land. How many spots are touching the table? (Figure 13)

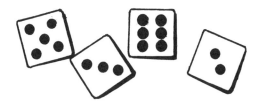

Figure 13

How many spots are hidden? (Figure 14)

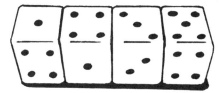

Figure 14

If two dice are rolled, what totals are possible and which is most likely to occur? (Figure 15)

Figure 15

Ask the children to make a tower from four dice. Can all four sides of the tower total the same? (Figure 16) The example shown below doesn't work!

Figure 16

Dice Games

Remind the children that the singular of dice is die. They can use manufactured dice but should also be encouraged to make their own from thick paper or card using one of the many nets of a cube. The traditional numbering system used on dice has opposite faces equal to seven. The number pairs for opposite faces are usually one and six, two and five and three and four. You could provide the children with blank dice ready for them to provide the numbers themselves. Interesting problem-solving tasks can be provided if the total of each of the opposite faces does not add up to seven.

NNSF links: Year 3: Investigate a general statement about familiar numbers. Year 4: Make and investigate a general statement about familiar numbers. Years 5 and 6: Same as Year 4.

Money Matters

Despite the fact that Egypt was the wealthiest country of the ancient world and that it carried out trade extensively with neighbouring regions it did not have currency. For buying and selling in the local market and to conduct foreign trade, a system of bartering was used. Some transactions could be carried out as a straight swap – for example, a goat could be worth a selection of fresh vegetables. Others were carried out through the use of metal weights made of gold, silver or copper, called deben, which weighed about 90 grams. This gave everything a value although the metal never actually changed hands. The seller would work out the value in terms of deben and the buyer would have to offer something worth this amount in exchange. For example, a bed might be worth two and half deben.

Workers were also paid in goods and then had to swap them for items they needed. Sailors working on Nile boats were paid in grain and then used quayside stalls to exchange it for food and clothing. Barter and exchange may still feature in some parts of Egypt but for tourists wishing to visit the country in order to find out about its diverse past, hard currency will definitely be needed.

Details of the money system that is used in Egypt today, and some problems connected with paying for a holiday there, are given on the photocopiable sheets: Money 1, 2 and 3 (pages 38–40). These cover converting our own currency into Egyptian pounds, changing money amounts into a range of different notes and costing out family holidays in Egypt.

Money Matters

Coins were gradually introduced into Egypt from about 380BC onwards when the country began to come under greater influence by invaders from Assyria, Persia and Greece. At present, the currency system is called the Egyptian pound and the most common notes in use are for 10, 20 and 50 Egyptian pounds. Solutions to the problems on the photocopiable sheets will vary depending on the rate of exchange at the time. Financial organisations will have up-to-date rates of exchange and many national newspapers also publish details daily. Children should become conversant with converting pounds into foreign currency and vice-versa. Some rounding off of amounts may be necessary in order to make numbers easier to work with in calculations. Other activities could include changing sums of spending money into Egyptian currency and making comparisons between Egyptian pounds and euros for those tourists coming from other European countries.

NNSF links: Year 3: Solve word problems involving numbers in 'real life' including money. Year 4: Use all four operations to solve word problems involving numbers in 'real life' including money. Year 5: As Years 3 and 4 but also including making simple conversions of pounds to foreign currency. Year 6: As previous years but also including making simple conversions of pounds to foreign currency and vice versa.

Vocabulary Box

archaeologist	doubling	random
barter	fraction	rate of exchange
bigger than	halving	ready reckoner
binary system	horizontal	regiment
charioteer	index finger	reign
company	infantry	scribe
consecutive number	inverse operation	smaller than
currency	negative number	square number
deben	ostraca	triangular number
dice	papyrus	tutor
decimal	Pascal's triangle	vertical
dice	perimeter	vizier
dictation	positive number	zero

Stacking Stones

○ Egyptian builders have a special way of multiplying if they want to calculate how many blocks of stone they have.

○ Here is an example. There are 15 blocks of stone in nine rows.

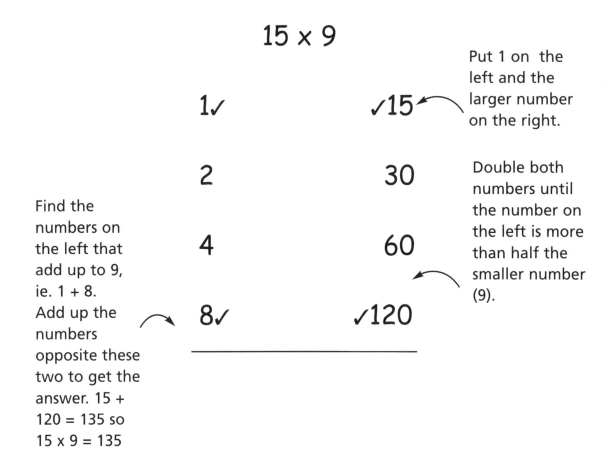

15 × 9

Put 1 on the left and the larger number on the right.

1✓   ✓15

2   30

Double both numbers until the number on the left is more than half the smaller number (9).

4   60

Find the numbers on the left that add up to 9, ie. 1 + 8. Add up the numbers opposite these two to get the answer. 15 + 120 = 135 so 15 x 9 = 135

8✓   ✓120

○ Now find how many blocks of stone the builders have collected here, using the Egyptian method of calculation shown above.

19 blocks of stone in 7 rows

21 blocks of stone in 8 rows

58 blocks of stone in 9 rows

83 blocks of stone in 6 rows

○ Show your calculations on the back of this sheet. Check your answers using a different method.

Block Builder

○ When Egyptian workers wanted to count up the number of stone blocks used in a building project, they used a special method of multiplication.

○ This is what they would do if they wanted to find out what was needed to build 36 blocks in a series of 9 rows.

$$36 \times 9$$

✓1   ✓36

Put 1 on the left and the larger number on the right.

2   72

Double both numbers until the number on the left is more than half the smaller number (9).

4   144

Find the numbers on the left that add up to 9, ie. 1 + 8. Add up the numbers opposite these two to get the answer.

✓8   ✓288
_____
9   324

○ Use this method of multiplying to find the number of stone blocks used in these building jobs.

     85 blocks in 8 rows

     96 blocks in 7 rows

     18 blocks in 15 rows

     44 blocks in 24 rows.

○ Show your calculations on the back of the sheet and then make up some of your own numbers for Egyptian multiplication.

Share Out

○ Ask your teacher to show you the special method of multiplying used by the Egyptians. It will involve doubling numbers.

○ Use this method to find the answers to these calculations. Check the answers by using another method of multiplying you have used.

28 x 14

36 x 21

57 x 34

65 x 48

○ A similar method can be used when dividing numbers. Hunefer the builder has to move 156 blocks of stone. He has six sleds to pull them on. How many stones will he put on each sled?

$$156 \div 6$$

Put 1 on the left and the smaller number on the right.

Double both numbers until the number on the right is more than half the larger number (156).

1	6
2	12✓
4	24
8	48✓
16	96✓

Find the numbers on the right that total 156, ie. 12 + 48 + 96 = 156. Add up the numbers opposite these to get the answer. 2 + 8 + 16 = 26

○ Now try these division calculations using the Egyptian system that is shown above. Remember to show your working out clearly and to check your answers by using another method of division.

112 ÷ 4   245 ÷ 7   392 ÷ 8

Brick Up

○ Complete the sequence of numbers found on these model pyramids that are made of six blocks of stone. Two numbers that are next to each other add up to make the number that comes above. An example has been done for you.

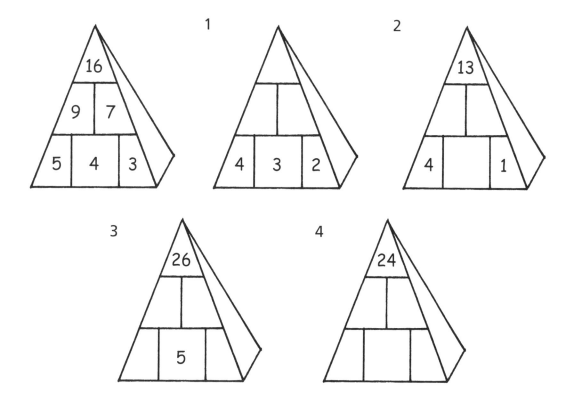

○ Use these blank pyramids to make up some of your own number sequences and ask your friend to try them out.

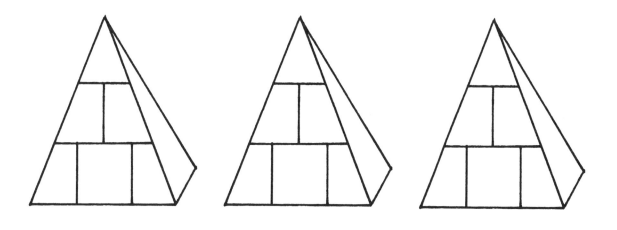

Climbing Point

○ These sequences are often called pyramid numbers because of the shapes they fit inside.

○ To make the sequences, two numbers next to each other are added to make the number that comes above. Investigate different ways to complete these six-brick pyramids. An example has been done for you.

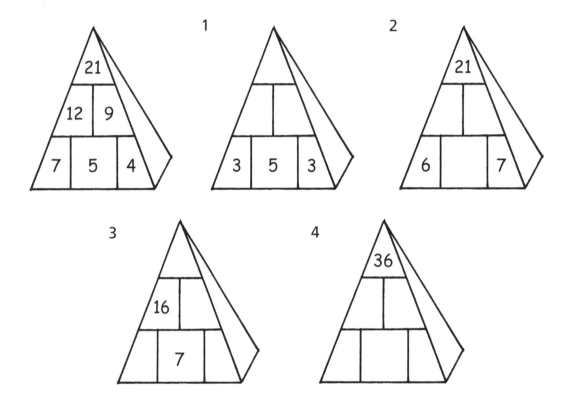

○ Now try these pyramids with ten bricks.

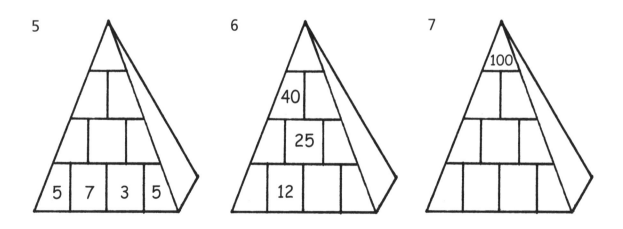

○ Try out some of your own pyramids on the back of the sheet.

Reach the Peak

○ These pyramid number sequences are written on ten bricks. Look at the example and explain to a friend how it has been made.

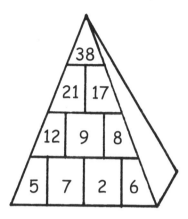

○ Investigate the different ways in which the number sequences in these pyramids have been made. Some include fractions and decimal numbers.

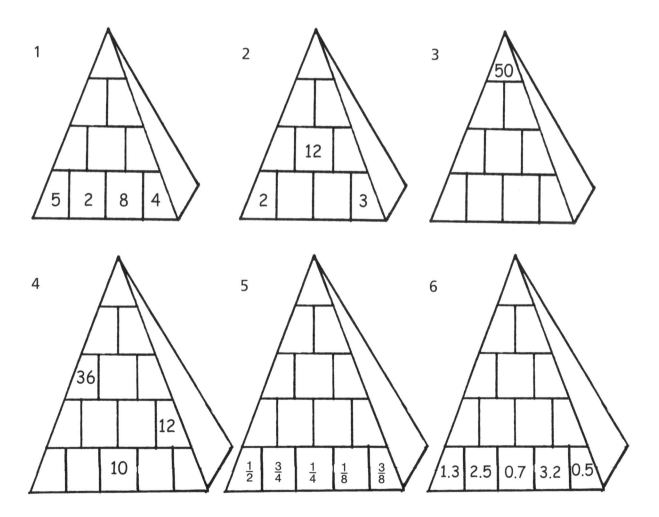

○ Try out some of your own pyramid number sequences on the back of the sheet.

All Change

○ If you went on holiday to Egypt, you would have to use Egyptian pounds.

£1 = 6 Egyptian pounds

○ How many Egyptian pounds would you get if you took these amounts of English money?

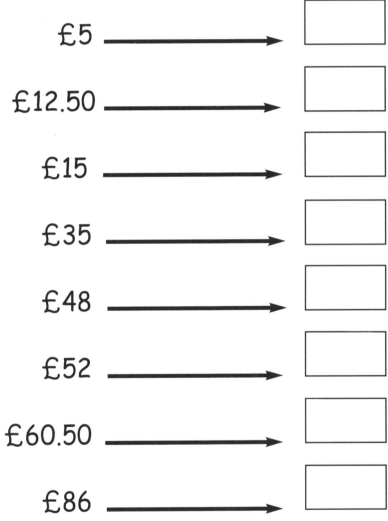

£5 ⟶ ☐

£12.50 ⟶ ☐

£15 ⟶ ☐

£35 ⟶ ☐

£48 ⟶ ☐

£52 ⟶ ☐

£60.50 ⟶ ☐

£86 ⟶ ☐

○ Find some books and holiday brochures about Egypt. What would you most like to see during your visit? What do you think you would spend most of your money on?

Big Spender

○ The Baxter family has decided to go on holiday to Egypt to see the famous historical sites like the Great Pyramid at Giza. They have to change their money into Egyptian pounds ready for spending while they are away.

○ Here is the current rate of exchange. How many Egyptian pounds will they get for their money.

$$£1 = 6 \text{ Egyptian pounds}$$

Mary wants to take £15
David wants to take £30
Joanne wants to take £33

Mum wants to take £450
Dad wants to take £600

○ Egyptian pounds come in 5, 10, 20, 50, 100 and 500 notes. Find at least two different ways of making up the amounts they have using these notes. For example, Mary will have 90 Egyptian pounds. She could have a 50 note and two 20 notes.

Mary _____

_____

David _____

_____

Joanne _____

_____

Mum _____

_____

Dad _____

_____

Historic Holiday

○ The Holloway family is going to Egypt for a holiday. There is Mr and Mrs Holloway, David who is 16, Sarah who is 12 and Stacey who is 5.

○ Below are some prices for package holidays to Egypt. Calculate how much each one will cost the family for a week-long stay.

Accommodation	Adults 7 nights	Children (under 16) 7 nights
HOTEL PYRAMID	499 BB	399
HOTEL NILE	529 HB	20% off adult price
HOTEL SPHINX	699 FB	30% off adult price
HOTEL PHARAOH	585 HB	349

All prices per person in £
BB = Bed and breakfast HB = Bed, breakfast and dinner FB = Bed and <u>all</u> meals

○ Which will be the most expensive holiday and how much will it cost?

○ Which will be the cheapest holiday and how much will it cost?

○ Which of the hotels would you choose for the family? Give your reasons.

○ How much spending money do you think the children need to take?

○ Find out the current rate of exchange and change the money into Egyptian pounds ready for the holiday.

Problem Solving

FACT **1** BOX

The Rhind Papyrus

The Rhind Mathematical Papyrus (RMP) is the most extensive and detailed of the three important documents that give us an insight into the range of mathematics carried out by the Ancient Egyptians. The document takes its name from a young Scottish lawyer called A H Rhind who spent some time in Egypt for health reasons and purchased the papyrus in 1858 after it had been discovered in some ruined buildings at Thebes. It was later brought to Britain and is now housed in the British Museum in London.

This particular papyrus contains 87 arithmetic and algebraic puzzles. They are written on 14 separate sheets of papyrus that each measure about 40cm wide by 32cm high. The document in total is about 5m in length. It is written in hieratic characters (a faster, shorthand version of hieroglyphics) and reads from right to left. The opening words of each problem are picked out in red ink and this has made it much easier for scholars to classify them.

Writing on the papyrus tells how it was copied by a scribe called Ahmose during the period of the Hyksos or Shepherd Kings around 1650BC, but that it contained work from 200 years earlier. There has been debate over the reasons why it was written although some believe it was really intended as a handbook or teaching manual used in the training of scribes. Some of the problems are introduced with the phrase, 'If a scribe says to you…'

Also discovered at the same time and in the same location as the Rhind Papyrus was the Egyptian Mathematical Leather Roll (EMLR). This item, also housed in the British Museum, measures about 40cm by 25cm and, although first found in 1858, was not successfully unrolled until 1927 because it was in such a brittle condition. It contains 26 calculations involving unit fractions and because each calculation was duplicated it has been possible to read them all clearly.

The third key document was originally called the Golenishchev Papyrus after the person who first purchased it in Egypt in 1893. But it is now most often referred to as the Moscow Mathematical Papyrus (MMP) since it has been kept at the Moscow Museum of Fine Arts since 1912. Only 8cm high but over 5m long, it outlines 25 problems involving such topics as the area of rectangles and triangles, the volume of a pyramid, equations, measurements of cloth and the rationing of loaves and beer. Unfortunately, because it is damaged, it is impossible to read some of the problems in full.

FACT **2** BOX

Divine rulers

Pharaohs (kings) ruled Egypt for over 3,000 years. The title comes from the word 'perao', meaning great house, and symbolised the wealth and power of the sovereign. Revered not only as a ruler but also worshipped as a god, the pharaoh owned the land, made the laws, levied the taxes, ordered the construction of buildings and, in many cases, personally led the army into battle. The line of pharaohs began around 3100BC when a ruler named Menes united the two regions of Egypt – the Lower Kingdom around the mouth of the River Nile and the Upper Kingdom further to the south. Around 2500BC, there followed the pharaohs Khufu, Khafra and Menkaura who were responsible for building the world's most famous pyramids at Giza.

One of the most formidable of all the pharaohs was Ramasses II. He reigned for 67 years between 1290BC and 1223BC. Ramasses was responsible for some of the greatest building programmes of any ruler, including the rock-cut temple at Abu Simbel and the Great Hall at Karnak. He was also a great warrior. His most famous victory was against the Hittites at Kadesh in 1285BC.

Perhaps the most radical of the pharaohs was Amenhotep IV who also became known as Akhenaten. Ruler between 1352BC and 1336BC, he banned all the traditional gods of the Egyptians and ordered the worship of one god only – the sun god, Aten. He set up a new capital city at Armana and closed down the temples of all the other gods. He was helped in this venture by his wife Nefertiti. After their deaths, the pharaohs who succeeded them soon restored the old gods, and the names of Akhenaten and Nefertiti became so hated that they were removed from many inscriptions.

It was rare that the pharaoh was a woman, but two of them have become particularly famous. Hatshepsut helped her young stepson to govern Egypt but she soon took full charge and ruled between 1473BC and 1458BC. Considered to be the last of Egypt's pharaohs is Cleopatra. She enlisted the help of the Roman general Julius Caesar to help her win the crown from her brother Ptolemy.

Of all the pharaohs, none is more famous now than one of Egypt's youngest ever rulers. He was the boy king Tutankhamun who only spent nine years on the throne between the ages of 9 and 18. The archaeologist Howard Carter discovered his tomb in the Valley of the Kings in 1922. The final resting place that had remained almost untouched by robbers for over 3,000 years, contained some 5,000 objects including weapons, clothes, furniture and jewellery as well as the king's famous coffins and mask.

Problem Solving

Think of a Number

A selection of puzzles found in the Rhind Mathematical Papyrus come in the 'think of a number' category. Use this type of puzzle to strengthen the children's use of vocabulary connected with number families, such as 'odd', 'even', 'square', 'factor' and 'multiple' and number operations like 'difference', 'product' and 'divisible by'. For example: I am the number that is the product of seven and five (35). I am an even number less than 30 but more than 20; I am a multiple of four and my digits total ten (28). Starting the task with the phrase 'If a scribe says to you…' will give it an even more authentic ring (see Fact box 1 on page 41).

There are also arithmetic progressions in the Rhind Papyrus that can be linked to finding the missing items in number patterns and sequences involving single and two-step operations. Equations also feature in the document – you could reinforce the work carried out on algebra in Chapter 1. Many of the later puzzles focus on the division of commodities among groups of people and the amount or proportion each is to receive. Again some reference has been made to these problems in Chapter 1.

The opportunity for children to sample puzzles linked to those in the Rhind Papyrus is given on photocopiable sheets: Number Puzzles 1, 2 and 3 (pages 50–52).

Think of a Number

When children are working on puzzles of this kind, challenge them not only to find answers but also to consider what strategies are being used to find them. Encourage them to discuss the questions 'What shall we try next?' and 'How did we work out the answer?' Remind them that combinations of mental methods, the use of jottings and more formal calculations are all legitimate ways of arriving at the correct solutions. It may be useful to work in reverse on some occasions. For example, provide a number and ask the children to make up clues about it or give them a completed number pattern and ask them to explain what rules have been followed to construct it.

Also, use the opportunity in number work of this kind to encourage the children to check their answers by using other methods. Ask them to estimate first by using approximations, then use inverse operations and check with equivalent calculations where appropriate.

NNSF links: Year 3: Solve mathematical problems and puzzles. Year 4: Explain methods and reasoning about numbers orally and in writing. Years 5 and 6: As Year 4 and also suggest extensions asking 'What if…?'

Through the Maze

The pyramid builders went to elaborate lengths to prevent the tombs inside them from being robbed of their precious treasures. They created false doors or made entrances out of huge lumps of granite so they were extremely difficult to move. But the most favourite ploy, especially by rulers during the Middle Kingdom (c2040–1640BC), was to create a system of false passageways, tunnels and corridors in an effort to confuse intruders. Unfortunately, these mazes were rarely successful and by 1000BC most of the notable tombs in Egypt had been plundered. The children can develop important movement and direction strategies if they are encouraged to create their own mazes. A simple example is given in Figure 1.

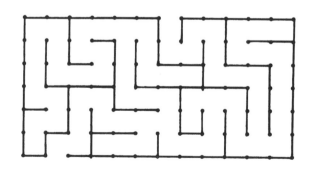

Figure 1

Extend this work to showing children how to plot a set of repeated digits. In Figure 2, for example, 233 is being used.

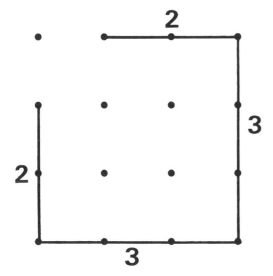

Figure 3.2

It should be continued until the shape is complete as shown in Figure 3.

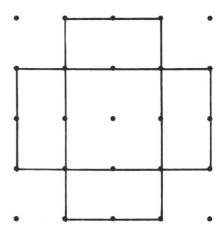

Figure 3.3

Certain important rules must be followed to complete the pattern. The first move must always be to the right. A turn is made for each new digit, going 90 degrees clockwise. The digit 3 does not mean linking three dots; it means drawing a straight line between the dots through three spaces. Sometimes lines may go over ones previously drawn. Challenge the children to try other patterns like 123, 623 and 342. Is an identical shape produced if the same digits are rearranged in a different order? Check with 124, 241 and 412.

Through the Maze

The children will be able to complete their mazes more easily and quickly if they use squared or dotty paper. Initially, start and finish points can be marked but these could be left out once they become more skilled with the processes involved. Alternatively, large nail boards and coloured string could be used or, for those keen to work on a larger scale, lines could be marked out with chalk on the playground or cones/marker flags could be used on the field. Children may be familiar with well-known mazes such as the labyrinth on the island of Crete in the Greek legend and examples in this country, like those at Ely Cathedral and Hampton Court.

The movement activity involving repeated digits will only work if the rules are followed closely. Practice is needed.

For further extension, try the following problems. It is said that many four-digit patterns produce open designs that do not return to the starting point. Test out this theory by using examples such as 2113 and 3211. The children may also be interested in going on to consider network problems including the Bridges of Konigsberg problem that was eventually solved by the famous Swiss mathematician Leonhard Euler. (There are a variety of websites containing the problem and its answer. Key in 'Bridges of Konigsberg' into your search engine.)

NNSF links: Year 3: Make and describe right-angled turns. Year 4: Recognise positions and directions. Years 5 and 6: As Year 4.

Senet

Archaeological evidence including artefacts and paintings suggest that senet was among the most popular of the board games enjoyed by the Ancient Egyptians. Four sets of the game were found in the tomb of Tutankhamun. One version, made from ebony and ivory, was complete with a drawer for the pieces and table legs shaped like those of a bull. The basic playing board consists of 30 squares – three rows with ten squares in each. Current-day experts are not completely sure how senet was played except to say that as well as providing entertainment, the game was also intended to convey a message in

that it symbolised the struggle between good and evil. The two players had to face the possible dangers that could befall a person as they attempted to reach the kingdom of the god Osiris. In Ancient Egypt, moves were determined by throwing coloured casting or throwing sticks (or knucklebones). Our equivalent today would be the use of dice.

A blank playing board and some suggestions about how the children might play the game are given on the photocopiable sheet: Games 3 (page 55).

Senet

Because no one is certain how this game was played, ask the children to make up their own rules for using the basic equipment and format of the game. In simple terms, senet could be played rather like a game of snakes and ladders with a coloured counter moving the number of places decided by the throw of a dice. Some of the squares could be illustrated as 'good' squares that would move the player on while 'bad' squares would hold them back. These squares should have an Ancient Egyptian context. For example, 'good' squares might include 'a successful grain harvest' and 'extra workers arrive for a building project'. 'Bad' squares might be 'attacked by a crocodile' or 'River Nile floods too high'. The shorter version of the game would take players from start to finish using two of the rows (as below).

Longer alternatives might include the introduction of extra pieces for each player, like the characters on a chessboard, and incorporating all the squares (as below).

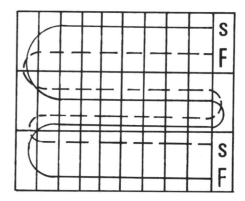

Here the aim might be to remove all the opponents' pieces from the board while preventing them from doing the same to you.

NNSF links: Year 3: Solve mathematical problems or puzzles, recognise simple patterns and relationships. Year 4: Solve mathematical problems or puzzles, recognise and explain patterns and relationships, generalise and predict. Years 5 and 6: Same as Year 4.

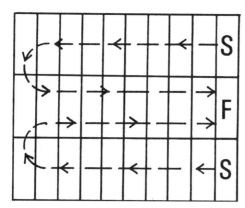

S = Start   F = finish

Snake Game

This game has been depicted in tomb paintings and versions have also been found carved into blocks of stone. It has been given the title 'The snake game' because its shape resembles the coiled body of a snake. The number of different segments determines the length of the game. Again, precise rules are uncertain but the aim appears to be to move a counter from the snake's tail to its head.

A dice is used to determine the number of moves made. In the stone version, grooves were cut so that a small stone ball could be used to indicate the moves made. Examples of these have been found with the pharaoh's name inscribed on them.

The children can make their own copy of this game using photocopiable sheet: Games 1 (page 53).

Snake Game

Some evidence suggests that this game may have originally been played with six counters. The children could play in pairs but might want to extend the game to involve six individual players, two teams of three, or three teams of two. If teams are involved, all members of the group would need to reach the finish before being declared the winner.

NNSF links: Years 3,4,5 and 6: See previous activity.

Alquerque

This game has long been popular throughout North Africa and the Middle East. A game board for it was found engraved in the temple at Al-Qurna on the west bank of the River Nile. It has been suggested that this and other game boards found on the site may have been carved by stonemasons eager to spend their spare time usefully while working on the construction of the building. The Arabic name for

the game is Elquirkat and it was when it was taken by North African invaders to Spain that the title Alquerque was adopted. Many other strategy games popular in other parts of Europe have been developed from it, including draughts.

A copy of the game board is provided for the children on the photocopiable sheet: Games 2 (page 54). The rules are outlined in the teachers' notes that follow.

Alquerque

Games of this kind provide a fun way for children to acquire and develop mathematical problem-solving skills. Encourage them to try out a variety of strategies and extend their logical thinking while playing. The game has two players who start with 12 counters each. The rules are as follows.

1 Start with the counters arranged on the board as shown on page 54. The players move their counters in turn in any direction to an empty adjacent point.

2 If a player finds an opponent's counter with a space next to it, they jump over and capture it.

3 Failing to take the chance to jump over the opponent's counter means that the player's counter is captured.

4 The winner of the game is the first player to take all the other player's counters.

NNSF links: Years 3,4,5 and 6: See previous activity.

More Games

As well as the board games that have already been mentioned, the Egyptians, young and old, were fond of playing games of all kinds. Paintings show children playing leapfrog and tug-of-war. Throwing and catching a ball was also extremely popular, not just in the standing position but also riding on someone else's back or jumping high into the air. A game similar to noughts and crosses was carved on an Egyptian temple in about 1400BC and examples of spinning tops have been discovered in a number of different locations.

Once the children have tried out some games of noughts and crosses, a variation on the same theme can be provided by the game called 'Three in a row'. Start with a 3 x 3 grid. The aim is to find how many crosses can be placed in the grid without getting three in a line. Extend the activity to try out 4 x 4, 5 x 5 and 6 x 6 grids. Encourage the children to look for a pattern in the possible solutions.

You could show the children how to make some home-made spinning tops from card and cocktail sticks (Figure 4), and use them for probability tasks.

Figure 4

What are the odds of throwing, for example, a 2 or a 6? What are the odds of throwing either an odd or an even number? Does the number of spins tried affect the accuracy of the result? Ask the children if they can place the likely outcomes on a probability line with impossible at one end and certain at the other (Figure 5).

Impossible   *Certain*

Figure 5

More Games

Use the noughts and crosses games not so much to determine who wins but as a starting point for discussing and trying out which strategies are best. Are the odds always heavily stacked in favour of the player who goes first? Is attack the best method of success or can victory be achieved by defending against the moves being made by the other player? Possible solutions for the 'Three in a row' game are given below although there will be alternatives.

3 x 3   4 x 4   5 x 5

In the spinner activities, the chance of throwing any single number, say 5, should be one-sixth. If the spinner is tried 24 times for example, you might expect the number 5 to come up four times. The chances of throwing an odd or an even number should be three-sixths since 1, 3 and 5 appear and so do 2, 4 and 6. This is often referred to as an even chance. On the probability line, 8 would be impossible because it does not appear on the spinner while a number between 1 and 6 would be certain. Encourage the children to compare the expected number of times a digit should occur with the actual number of times it happens. Is it true to say that the more times the activity is carried out the nearer the actual result should be to the expected outcome? Does this require 20, 50 or even 100 tries?

NNSF links: Year 3: Solve a given problem by organising and interpreting numerical data in simple lists. Year 4: As Year 3. Year 5: Discuss the chance or likelihood of particular events. Year 6: Use the language associated with probability to discuss events, including those with equally likely outcomes.

Telling the Time

Using the movement of the Sun during the day and the position of the stars at night, the Egyptians were among the first peoples to attempt the accurate measurement of time. They were quickly able to arrive at a period of 24 hours – 12 hours of darkness, 10 hours of light and an hour at either end for twilight. Because of seasonal differences, hours were often of unequal length but agreement was reached about 24 equal hours by 1300BC and it was later civilisations, like the Greeks, that adopted this system. In Ancient Egypt, standard intervals of time were measured by the flow of water through a hole in a large vessel. Because of the climate, sundials were also used and these proved to be more accurate than water clocks. A simple example of a water clock that children can construct is shown in Figure 6.

Pour in water and time its descent into jug at the bottom.

Figure 6

Make a centimetre scale on the bottom cup. Put a finger over the hole in the top cup and fill it with water. When the finger is removed, the water will drip through the containers. Times can be recorded for the first drop of water to reach the bottom, water reaching the first centimetre mark, and so on.

The children could also try a variation of an Egyptian shadow clock (Figure 7).

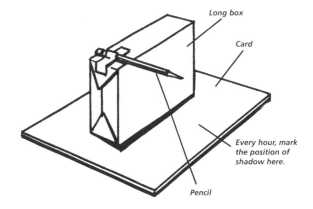

Long box

Card

Every hour, mark the position of shadow here.

Pencil

Figure 7

Fix a pencil across the top of a long box. Place it outside on a piece of cardboard on a sunny day in such a way that the pencil's shadow is perpendicular to the box. Mark the position of the shadow every hour. The best results will be obtained early in the morning or late in the afternoon.

Telling the Time

The science of time-keeping by using water is known as clepsydra, from the Greek word meaning 'water thief'. Point out to the children that simple water clocks do not allow for the fact that as water escapes through the holes pressure is reduced so slowing down the flow of water and increasing the time taken. Using a container with sloping sides helps and water clocks will certainly produce an approximate guide.

As well as having plenty of water and plenty of sunshine, Egypt also had plenty of sand. Sand timers are popular in school for use in practical maths activities and science experiments. Set children the problem-solving task of developing a

clock using sand and comparing its accuracy with the other two methods already suggested. While times are being recorded, make links between the 12-hour and 24-hour clock systems. Some children may be interested in finding out the time differences between their homes in Britain and those in Egypt today.

NNSF links: Year 3: Use units of time and the relationship between them. Suggest suitable units to measure time. Year 4: Estimate and check times using seconds, minutes and hours. Year 5: Use units of time. Read and use 24-hour clock notation. Year 6: As above. Appreciate different times around the world.

Building Bricks

Much of the house building in Ancient Egypt was carried out using regular-sized rectangular bricks. They were made from River Nile mud that, after being tipped into a mould, was allowed to bake in the hot sun. Straw and pebbles were often added to give the bricks strength.

Houses for most people were small, box-like constructions. The flat roof, complete with air vents, was also made from mud, supported by wooden beams. An outside staircase was usually added so that the roof, where it might be cooler, could be used for eating and sleeping. Windows were small and high up so they would not let in too much sunshine. The outside of the building was whitewashed to reflect strong sunlight while canopies, climbing plants and trees were grown in courtyard areas to provide as much shade as possible. Wall and floor tiling was used inside larger houses belonging to wealthier residents, especially in bathrooms and kitchens where water might spoil the mud-brick surfaces.

Patterns and murals were common on the walls of these houses to brighten up the interior. Working in two-dimensions first of all, ask the children to investigate the different ways in which rectangles will tessellate. Switch to three-dimensions by making miniature clay bricks using a mould. Build these into walls to see which makes the strongest construction.

Ideas and suggestions for activities are given on photocopiable sheets: Tessellation 1, 2 and 3 (pages 56–58).

Building Bricks

Squared paper will speed up the process when children are testing out tessellation using squares and rectangles. Alternatively, they can make templates to draw round. Two-dimensional shapes need to be categorised into three families. There will be those that tessellate on their own, like squares and rectangles, those that tessellate with help, like hexagons, and those that will not tessellate, like circles.

Encourage the children to explain the different bricklaying designs like stretcher bond, English bond and Flemish bond (see page 56), and why they make good methods of building. The word 'bond' actually means to make a strong join.

Point out the extent to which bricks and tiles are still used in building today. Ask the children to look for examples in their own environment and collect evidence about the tessellation involved when walls and floors are put together.

NNSF links: Year 3: Investigate a general statement about familiar shapes. Year 4: Make and investigate a general statement about familiar shapes by finding examples that satisfy it. Years 5 and 6: As Years 3 and 4.

Vocabulary Box

adjacent	horizontal	reflect
algebra	impossible	reign
Alquerque	inscription	right-angle
approximation	jotting	segment
bonding	labyrinth	senet
certain	maze	square number
clepsydra	mould	suicide
divisibility	multiple	sundial
English bond	network	stretcher bond
equation	odd	tessellate
equivalent calculation	papyrus	three-dimensional (3D)
even chance	parallel	two-dimensional (2D)
factor	Pharaoh	unit fraction
Flemish bond	probability	vertical
hieratic	product	water clock

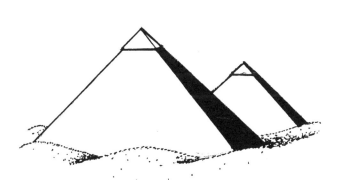

On the Farm

○ Rahotep the farmer has been writing down some calculations on his papyrus. But the rain has made the ink run.

○ Find the missing numbers that have now ended up as ink blots. Our number system is being used here to make the calculations easier.

Grain harvest

$$15 + \blacksquare = 39 \qquad 57 - \blacksquare = 12$$

$$\blacksquare + 19 = 50 \qquad \blacksquare + \blacksquare = 75$$

$$\blacksquare - 12 = 47 \qquad \blacksquare - \blacksquare = 31$$

Date picking

$$5 \times \blacksquare = 40 \qquad 54 \div \blacksquare = 6$$

$$\blacksquare \times 4 = 48 \qquad \blacksquare \times \blacksquare = 24$$

$$15 \times \blacksquare = 90 \qquad \blacksquare \div \blacksquare = 11$$

Wine making

○ Help Rahotep find the missing number that is the answer to these word problems.

1 I am the total of 15 jars, 23 jars and 19 jars. What am I?

2 I am the difference between 84 jars and 27 jars. What am I?

3 I am the product of 12 jars and 9 jars. What am I?

4 I am an odd number of jars. I come between 40 jars and 50 jars. I am a multiple of seven. What am I?

All in Sequence

○ Nakt the scribe has been working on some problems about number sequences that he is going to use to test his pupils.

○ Fill in the missing numbers in the number sequences. Then write the rule that is being used. Remember: some of them may have a two-step rule.

| 1 | 8 | 15 | 22 | 29 | _____ | _____ | Rule: |

| 97 | 88 | 79 | 70 | 61 | _____ | _____ | Rule: |

| 4 | 8 | 16 | 32 | 64 | _____ | _____ | Rule: |

| 121 | 100 | 81 | 64 | 49 | _____ | _____ | Rule: |

| -13 | -10 | -7 | -4 | -1 | _____ | _____ | Rule: |

| 25 | 30 | 28 | 33 | 31 | _____ | _____ | Rule: |

| 63 | 54 | 46 | 39 | 33 | _____ | _____ | Rule: |

| 12.7 | 14.2 | 15.7 | 17.2 | 18.7 | _____ | _____ | Rule: |

○ Here is a number sequence from the Rhind Papyrus (Problem 40):

1   4   7   10   13

The numbers go up in threes. The total of the last three numbers, 7 + 10 + 13 = 30. This is six times the total of the first two numbers, 1 + 4 = 5.

○ Now try this sequence:

1   14   27   40   53

What is the pattern this time? Can you apply a similar formula to the Rhind Papyrus one above?

○ Think up your own sequence puzzles like this. The number in the formula that you multiply by may vary each time.

Solve It

○ Nakt the scribe has given his trainee scribes some number problems to work on. He wants to see how good their mathematical skills have become. These are like Problems 30–34 in the Rhind Papyrus.

○ Here are the first group of problems.

1 Think of a number. Its half and its quarter added together makes nine. What is the number?

2 Think of a number. Its two-thirds and its half added together make 42. What is the number?

3 Think of a number. Its quarter, its half and its eighth added together make 14. What is the number?

4 Think of a number. Its two-thirds, its tenth and its fifth added together make 87. What is the number?

○ Here is a puzzle like Problem 28 in the Rhind Papyrus. Try this with multiples of 3 up to 100. Does it always work?

Take the multiple of 3. Find two-thirds of it and add it on. Take away a third of this total. Then take a tenth of this away. What are you left with?

Here are two examples. Start with 9. Find two-thirds and add 9 + 6 = 15. Take away a third of this total 15 – 5 = 10. Find a tenth of this and take away again 10 – 1 = 9. You are back the number you started with. Now try 27. Find two-thirds and add 27 + 18 = 45. Take a third away from this total 45 – 15 = 30. Find a tenth of this and take away again 30 – 3 = 27.

○ Finally, try a modern version of Problem 79 in the Rhind Papyrus.

As I was going to St Ives I met a man with seven wives. Each wife had seven houses. Each house had seven cats. Each cat chased seven mice. Each mouse ate seven ears of corn. Each ear had seven morsels of new grain. How much grain could be saved if the mice were caught?

(Multiply the number of houses by the number of cats by the number of mice by the number of ears of corn by the number of morsels, ie. 7 x 7 = 49 x 7, and so on. But is there a quicker way to work it out?)

Snake Charmer

○ This a traditional game from Ancient Egypt. It is called the snake game because it takes place on the coiled body of a serpent. The game will last longer if you mount it on thick cardboard and cover it with plastic.

○ Each player needs a different coloured counter. Take it in turns. Throw a dice to get your score each time. Count your moves around the small circles on the snake's body. The winner is the first person to reach the snake's head. You have to start again if you land on a circle already containing someone else's counter.

Finish here

Start here

Alquerque

○ Stonemasons are thought to have played this game to while away their spare time when they were working on building projects in Ancient Egypt.

○ Make two copies of the grid below and mount them on card to make a sqaure board. Cover the board with plastic and then cut it out. You will then be able to play the game over and over again.

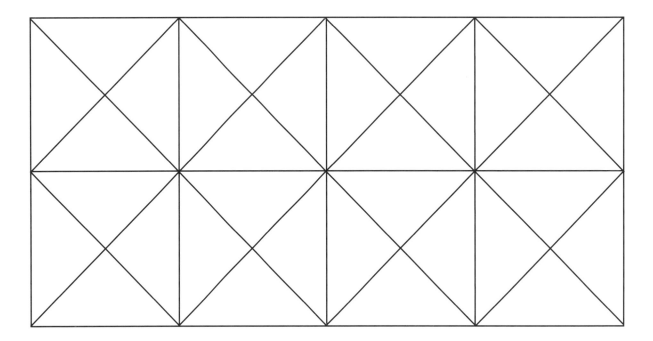

RULES

1 Play in pairs.

2 Each player has 12 counters and chooses their own colour.

3 Set up the counters as shown in the diagram on the right.

4 Players move counters in turn in any direction to an empty adjacent point.

5 If a player finds an opponent's counter next to it, they must jump over and capture it.

6 If they miss the chance to do this their counter is captured. The winner is the first player to capture all their opponent's counters.

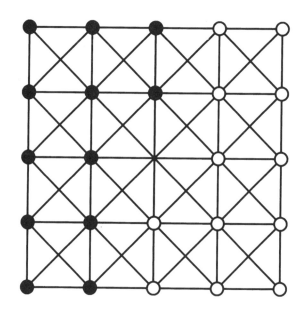

Senet

○ Four different sets of this game called senet were found in the tomb of the boy pharaoh Tutankhamun. One set was made of ebony and ivory.

○ No one is exactly sure how the game was played. The basic playing board is shown below but you can make up your own rules.

○ You could use counters to show the moves you make and a dice to decide the number of moves. Rather like snakes and ladders, make up squares that will help you on or move you back. Some examples are given. You will also have to decide how long the game will be and where it will start and finish. You may also want to introduce other pieces that can be captured when a player lands on them, like in the game of chess.

	Poor grain harvest. Go back 6.					Extra workers arrive at temple. Go on 8.			
			Trading ship arrives in port. Go on 5.						
Chased by a crocodile. Go back 4.			Houses flooded by the Nile. Go back 3.		Find new stone quarry. Go on 10.				

House Builder

○ Amosis the house builder uses bricks he makes from the mud of the River Nile.

○ The bricks have to be bonded together to make walls strong. The joints between them where the mortar goes should not be next to each other.

○ Here are some examples of brick bonding that are used nowadays. Make some brick-shaped templates out of cardboard and try them out.

Brick positions
This way is called stretcher.   This way is called header.

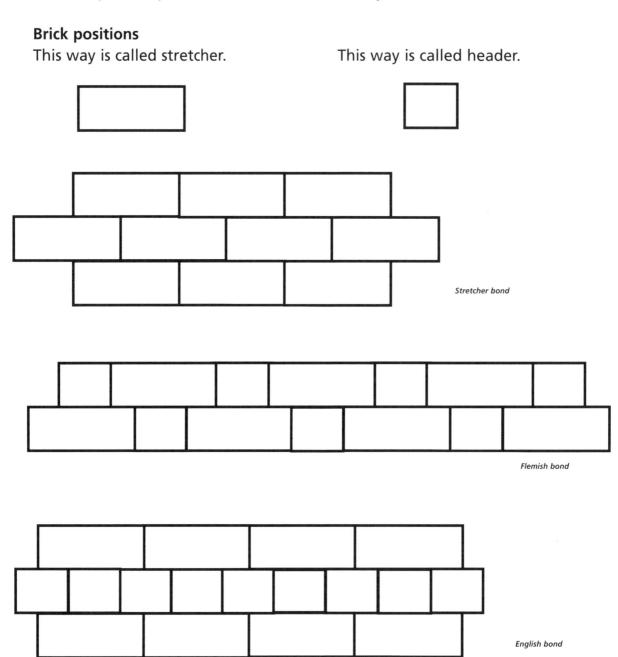

Stretcher bond

Flemish bond

English bond

○ Use the cardboard templates to make some tessellating brick patterns of your own.

Bathroom Tiles

○ Mosi and his wife Stery have a new house. They decide to have some coloured tiles on the bathroom walls to stop the mud bricks from being splashed.

○ The square tiles form a tessellating pattern that will also have reflective or mirror symmetry.

○ The patterns below have been started already. The lines of symmetry are shown. Help Mosi and his wife to complete them.

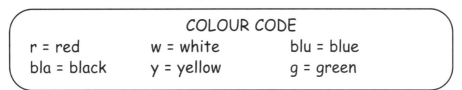

COLOUR CODE

r = red   w = white   blu = blue
bla = black   y = yellow   g = green

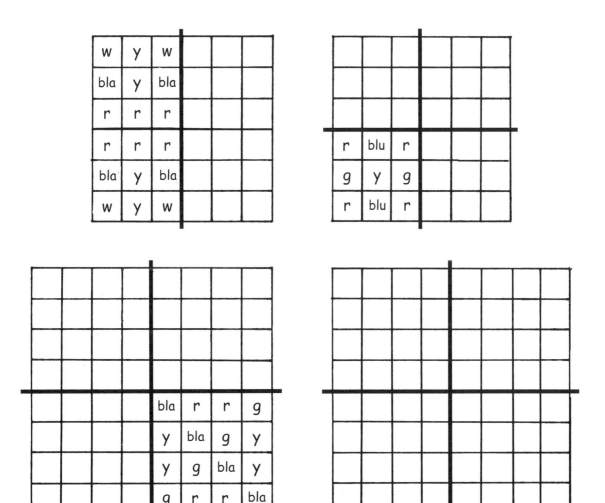

○ Make up your own tessellating symmetrical design in the blank grid above.

Bright Kitchen

○ Mosi and Stery want to make a patterned frieze of tiles for the kitchen in their new house to stop the mud bricks from being splashed.

○ Here is the patterned square tile that they will use.

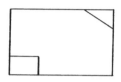

○ Cut out some large squares and mark them with the design. Then by rotating or reflecting them, make an interesting pattern for the kitchen wall. Here is one possibility. It may help to try out your patterns on squared paper.

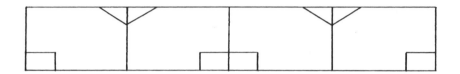

○ Cut out cardboard versions of these unusual shapes and use them to make other interesting tessellating patterns.

1

2
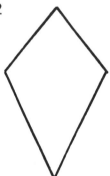

3
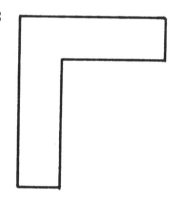

4
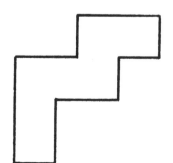

5
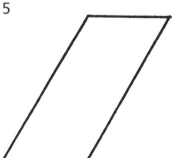

Handling Data

FACT BOX 1

Egypt – then and now

Egypt is situated on the north-eastern tip of Africa. The Mediterranean Sea forms its northern boundary and the Red Sea fringes much of its eastern edge. To the south lies Sudan and in the west, Egypt shares its border with Libya. Its history covers a vast span of time if you consider that the ruler Cleopatra (51–30BC) is closer in time to us today than she was to the pharaohs who built the first pyramids.

In ancient times both Memphis, near the delta of the Nile, and Thebes, now called Luxor, were awarded the status of capital city. Later, following invasion by the Greeks, Alexandria took over this role. When Arab conquerors came to Egypt in the seventh century, it was Cairo that became the chief city. It remains the capital and with a population of over 12 million it is the largest city not only in the Middle East but also in Africa. One of Cairo's most visited buildings is the Museum of Egyptian Antiquities where over 100 000 exhibits are on display including treasures from the tomb of Tutankhamun.

Originally, Ancient Egypt was made up of two kingdoms. Lower Egypt was the land around the Nile delta while Upper Egypt stretched along the Nile valley from Saqqara to Luxor. The two kingdoms were united by the pharaoh Menes in about 3100BC. Later pharaohs are often seen wearing the double crown of Egypt. It is made up of the bucket-shaped red crown of Lower Egypt and the bottle-shaped white crown of Upper Egypt.

Even from earliest times, Egypt was a trading nation. It exported surplus wheat and barley, linen, papyrus and rope. From Nubia to the south of Egypt came tusks, ostrich feathers and leopard skins. Silver came from Syria, cedar wood from Lebanon, and ebony and ivory from central Africa. Other traders went further afield to Cyprus, Crete and Greece. Some went as far as the country of Punt (now believed to be modern-day Somalia) for gold and incense. This arduous journey seems to have involved dismantling ships and carrying them across desert to reach the Red Sea, where they were reassembled for the journey south-east.

Today Egypt, ruled by its fourth president, Hosni Mubarak, illustrates the stark contrast between modern cities and industries and rural village life. An Islamic country with one of the fastest growing populations in the world, it occupies an important strategic position in Middle Eastern politics. Agriculture, tourism, textiles and chemicals are its main source of income while many Egyptians still leave the country to work in the oilfields of Libya and the Gulf states to send back money to their families.

FACT BOX 2

The River Nile

Rising in the mountains of central Africa, and flowing some 6,500km until it reaches the Mediterranean, the Nile is one of the world's longest rivers and one of few that flows from south to north. Its two most important tributaries are the White Nile and the Blue Nile, but for much of its length it has no tributaries at all. The river is famous for its delta – a system of channels that form close to its mouth as it flows into the Mediterranean. Without the river, people in ancient times would never have been able to settle in Egypt, a country that is 90 per cent desert. It not only gave them water and a means of transport but it also gave fish to catch, birds and animals to hunt, and plants to gather and use. Later, Egyptians developed the skill of tilling the rich silt deposited by the Nile's annual flood to grow crops on its banks, make pots and construct houses.

For thousands of years, the basic calendar of Egyptian life was based around the river. Towards the end of July, the Nile began to rise. During this season (called Akhet), land-workers were employed in construction projects building pyramids, temples or irrigation systems, or fought in the army. When the floodwaters began to recede between November and February (the season called Peret), crops were sown in the rich silt left behind. From March to June (the season called Shema), the barley, wheat and other crops were harvested and taken off to granaries for storage.

Whatever time of the year, the Nile would be teeming with boats of all descriptions. Small boats built from papyrus reeds were used for fishing and short journeys. Wooden boats made longer journeys but they needed to be kept lightweight so they could be carried around obstacles like waterfalls. Trading boats used a combination of sail and oar power, and strong wooden barges carried heavy blocks for limestone from the quarry to the building site. The most magnificent vessels were the pleasure boats of the pharaohs with their gold-covered cabins and sails of costly fabric.

The pattern of life set by the River Nile changed forever with the development of the Aswan High Dam in the 1960s. Building a large new dam at this point to control the flow of water established a massive new stretch of water named Lake Nasser after the Egyptian president of the day. It meant that the country could increase its food production to meet a growing population and could also produce much more electricity. But there was a price to pay. People whose towns and villages were swallowed up by the lake had to be re-housed and many tombs, temples and other remains, like those at Abu Simbel, had to be relocated.

Handling Data

Tally Charts

When finger counting became too difficult and an abacus was not available, scribes in Ancient Egypt resorted to some form of tallying method. Records show that the Egyptians were keen to gather a variety of statistics, especially when a census was being carried out or items, such as sheep in a flock or the total containers of grain stored in a granary, were being recorded for taxation purposes. Other situations where statistics were kept might have included a tally of construction workers engaged on building a tomb or temple, or the number of blocks of stone needed in pyramid construction.

Marks could have been scratched in the sand, on clay or wax tablets, or marked on ostraca-broken pieces of pottery or stone that were used for jotting down words or numbers before tidy versions were transferred to papyrus.

Use the tallying method for census-type activities in the classroom and around the school. For example, challenge the children to record the number of pupils in each class, the different ways in which children travel to school, what they do at lunchtime and which are the most popular school subjects, clubs and other activities.

Tally Charts

Remind the children that the tallying system is particularly useful when counting larger numbers. Revise the tallying method with the children. Four items are recorded by short vertical strokes while the fifth tally mark consists of a diagonal line across them. These so-called 'bundles of five' make it much easier to total up at the end of the count. (see diagram).

$\cancel{||||} = 5$

$\cancel{||||}\ \cancel{||||}\ \cancel{||||}\ || = 17$

NNSF links: Years 3, 4, 5 and 6: Solve a problem by representing and interpreting data in tally charts.

Distances and Directions

Encourage the children to work on aspects of distance and direction in both an ancient and a modern context. Involve the use of bar-line charts at the same time (as shown in Figure 1) as opposed to bar charts (as in Figure 4 on page 62).

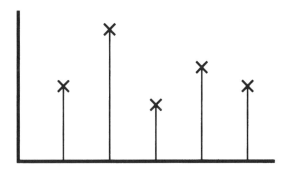

Figure 1

First, ask the children to locate positions, directions and distances covered when the traders from Ancient Egypt travelled to take their goods abroad. Check the locations mentioned in Fact box 1 on page 59, which include Syria, Lebanon, Cyprus, Greece and Punt (now called Somalia). Babylon (Iran) and Afghanistan could also be included.

Then help the children to investigate the routes taken and the distances travelled by the aircraft that fly from countries in Europe, including Britain, taking tourists to Egypt. The children can also make comparisons in chart form between the length of the River Nile and other major rivers in other parts of the world (see Figure 2).

The world's major rivers
(distances rounded off)

Nile	6,700km
Amazon	6,600km
Chang Jiang	6,300km
Mississippi–Missouri	6,000km
Ob-Irtysk	5,600km
Huang He	5,500km
Zaire	4,500km
Mekong	4,400km

Figure 2

Activities based on these themes can be found on the photocopiable sheets: Distance 1, 2 and 3 (pages 69–71).

Distances and Directions

You will need a selection of atlases and maps covering Africa, the Mediterranean region and Europe for the children to plot locations and work out the distances involved. Research skills like interrogating an index and using grids and co-ordinates to find places on a map may also need some revision. Take the opportunity to encourage the children to give the directions of routes according to an eight-point compass. Practice may be needed in reading map scales when accurate distances are being calculated. Point out to the children that the traders of Ancient Egypt would have used land and sea routes to reach their destinations while modern air travel follows a much more direct, 'as the crow flies' route.

Note: While on the subject of exploration and travel, the children may be interested in finding out more about the Norwegian explorer Thor Heyerdahl who built a boat out of papyrus reeds exactly like those used by the Ancient Egyptians. He attempted to sail it across the Atlantic in 1969–70. Challenge the children to find out whether he was successful, what he was trying to demonstrate, and why he called his boat Ra.

Squared paper will be required to provide a grid for the bar-line charts. Assistance may be needed when decisions have to be made about choosing suitable scales, and full labelling will be necessary. Bar-line charts are often referred to as 'stick' graphs because they are constructed using single lines. Stress to the children that in this case it is not appropriate to join the tops of the 'sticks' as each distance shown is a separate entity.

*NNSF links: Year 3: Solve a given problem by organising and interpreting numerical data in graphs. Measure using standard units. Read scales to the nearest division. Recognise and use the four compass directions. **Years 4, 5 and 6:** Solve a problem by presenting and interpreting data in bar-line charts. Use, read and write standard metric units. Record estimates and readings from scales to a suitable degree of accuracy. Use the eight compass directions.*

Population Figures

Modern-day Egypt has one of the most rapidly growing populations in the world. It is reckoned to be rising by about one million each year. There are two main reasons for this. Improvements in health mean that fewer babies die, and an increase in food production has been brought about by projects like the Aswan High Dam (see page 59). Rounded off population figures for each decade during the last century are given in Figure 3 and children can use these to practise their skills at making a bar chart (Figure 4).

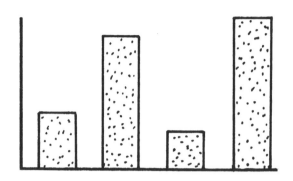

Figure 4

Egypt: population figures *(in millions)*

1900	10m	1960	25m
1910	12m	1970	33m
1920	14m	1980	43m
1930	15m	1990	50m
1940	17m	2000	54m
1950	20m		

Figure 3

It is not possible to know how many people would have lived in Egypt during the time of the pharaohs. But one fact is certain – because Egypt has always been mostly desert, the vast majority of the country's people have always lived in the Nile delta region and along the fertile strip within the valley of the river.

Population Figures

Provide squared paper for the children to create their bar graphs. This type of graph is sometimes referred to as a block or column graph because of the way the information is recorded. Some large figures are involved here so decisions will have to be made about the kind of squared paper used and what each square will represent. Also remind the children that graphs of all kinds need to be fully labelled. They should give the graph a title, label both axes carefully, and indicate what scale is being used. When it is complete, encourage the children to interrogate the graph for information.

To extend the activity, comparisons could be made between the population of Egypt and that of Britain, or between Cairo and London, or Cairo and the largest city to where the children live.

NNSF links: Years 3, 4, 5 and 6: Solve a given problem by organising and interpreting numerical data in bar charts.

Climate

The climate had an important influence on the inhabitants of Ancient Egypt. It has already been mentioned in Chapter 3 that buildings had air vents and small high windows in an effort to keep them cool (see page 48). Houses were also whitewashed to reflect the hot sun. Canopies were erected and plants and trees grown to provide shaded areas. Because of the high temperatures experienced during most of the year, people wore thin, loose-fitting clothing and open sandals.

Long days of sunshine helped crops to grow but, as we have seen, good supplies of water were also needed. Floodwater from the Nile was channelled through irrigation ditches and retained in small ponds, called catch basins, for when river levels returned to normal. Today, the climate permits visitors to Egypt to enjoy hot, dry conditions all year round so tourism is a year-long business. Average temperatures and daily hours of sunshine for each of the months are given in Figure 5.

Encourage the children to record climate information using line graphs, such as that in Figure 6.

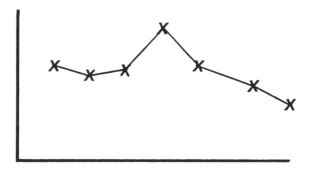

Figure 6

The opportunity to sample some climate activities is provided on the photocopiable sheets: Climate 1, 2 and 3 (pages 72–74).

Extension activities could include comparing the average temperatures for each month in Egypt with those in Britain.

Average temperatures and daily hours of sunshine (Cairo)

	Jan	Feb	Mar	Apr	May	Jun	July	Aug	Sept	Oct	Nov	Dec
°C	19	21	24	28	29	30	32	33	28	27	29	21
hrs	8	9	9	11	11	13	13	12	12	10	9	8

Figure 5

Climate

The temperatures given in Figure 5 are for the capital city Cairo. Children can use these or they could gather their own statistics. These are readily available in travel brochures or on the Internet. They should be aware that figures may vary in different parts of the country. In general, temperatures will be higher inland, at places like Luxor and Aswan, while Cairo will benefit from its proximity to the sea. Emphasise the points already made earlier in the chapter about making charts and graphs. If children ask about joining up the points recorded, explain that it might prove useful to show the trend of the temperatures as they move up and down but that intermediate points are not intended to show what the average temperature might have been halfway through a month.

NNSF links: Years 3, 4, 5 and 6: Solve a given problem by organising and interpreting numerical data in a line graph.

Conversion Graphs

One of the most important features of conversion graphs is that they can be used to investigate relationships. They are a quick and easy method of changing one set of units into another, especially where metric and imperial systems still run hand in hand. In the context of this topic, the three most appropriate graphs for the children to examine would be the conversion between British and Egyptian currency (unfortunately both called pounds), the measurement of distances in miles and kilometres, and the differences between recording temperatures on the Celsius and Fahrenheit scales.

Tables of figures to assist the children in making these graphs are given in Figures 7, 8 and 9.

£ to Egyptian pounds conversion										
£	1	2	3	4	5	6	7	8	9	10
E£	6	12	18	24	30	36	42	48	54	60

Figure 7

Miles to kilometres conversion										
miles	6	12	19	25	31	37	43	50	56	62
km	10	20	30	40	50	60	70	80	90	100

Figure 8

Celsius to Fahrenheit conversion (°C to °F)										
°C	7	10	13	16	19	22	25	28	31	34	37
°F	45	50	55	61	66	72	77	82	88	93	99

Figure 9

Conversion Graphs

Many adults in this country still talk about distance in terms of miles and speed in terms of miles per hour. Converting pounds sterling into Egyptian pounds is something that every tourist from this country needs to get used to. Some children may also be keen to see how the Euro will change into Egyptian pounds. Up-to-date exchange rates can be obtained from banks, building societies and the Post Office. Alternatively, they are often published in national newspapers.

Provide a range of different kinds of squared paper. Remind the children that graphs will start at zero and will form a straight line because quantities will increase by the same amount each time. This is known as constant proportion. Points should be located as accurately as possible and then connected with a line drawn with a ruler. Make sure that the children appreciate that this is a type of line graph in which intermediate values have significant meaning.

One of the graphs is given as an example in the diagram below. The Celsius scale was previously known as Centigrade and is now the most common system used in the world. However, the Fahrenheit scale is still favoured in some places, particularly the USA and Canada.

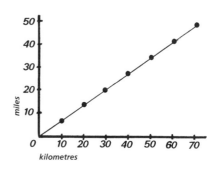

NNSF links: Years 3, 4 and 5: Solve a problem by organising and interpreting numerical data in tables and graphs. Year 6: Solve a problem by representing, extracting and interpreting data in tables, graphs, charts and diagrams including a conversion graph.

Seasonal Graphs

In Fact Box 2 on page 59, details are given of the three-season year in Ancient Egypt when activities were very much influenced by the habits of the River Nile. 'Akhet' was the season of flooding, 'Peret' the time for planting and 'Shema' when crops were harvested. The most appropriate way to show this type of information is in a pie chart. Based on a circle, the pie chart has become an increasingly popular way of showing information because it has visual appeal.

Point out to the children that they will need to divide up the chart into three sectors to illustrate the seasons. These could be illustrated. The months can be labelled around the circumference. This type of graph is particularly good at showing how part of something relates to the whole. The children could also make a pie chart showing the cycle of seasons in their own country and relate it to farming activities so that comparisons can be made.

Seasonal Graphs

Encourage the children to make comparisons between the pie chart and the other types of graph that have been made so far in this chapter. Discuss the meaning of the word 'cycle' in this context – a series of events that happen in the same order over and over again. Some children may need help to divide the circle into three equal thirds but those with some knowledge of angles should be able to use a protractor to measure the 120 degrees needed (360 degrees divided by 3). Extend the mathematical process involved here by examining cause and effect. The cycle continued to operate if the Nile flooded the optimum amount. But what happened if the floodwaters were far less than expected or if they rose so high that too much land was swamped? What effect might this have for the people of Ancient Egypt in the coming year?

NNSF links: Years 3, 4, 5 and 6: Solve a problem by collecting, organising, representing, extracting and interpreting data in tables, graphs and charts, including pie charts.

Timelines

Because of the vast span of time covered by any study of Ancient Egypt, timelines are an excellent way of showing important data. They also illustrate a key area where mathematics and history merge closely together. Some of the key dates that could be used in timeline activities are given in Figures 10 and 11.

Leading pharaohs

Khufu	2551–2528BC
Pepy I	2289–2255BC
Hatshepsut	1473–1458BC
Akhenaten	1353–1335BC
Tutankhamun	1333–1323BC
Ramasses II	1290–1224BC
Alexander the Great	332–323BC
Cleopatra	51–30BC

Figure 10

Periods in Egyptian history

Predynastic	3500–3200BC
Early dynastic	3200–2700BC
Old Kingdom	2700–2180BC
First Intermediate Period	2180–2040BC
Middle Kingdom	2040–1640BC
Second Intermediate Period	1640–1570BC
New Kingdom	1570–1080BC
Late Period	1080–330BC
Greek–Roman Period	330–30BC

Figure 11

Alternatively, the children could draw up timelines based on their own areas of research. Time spans are immense in this topic so fields of study should be narrowed down, especially with younger children. Dates should not become an obsession and the emphasis should be on the sequence in which events happened. This will help to improve children's appreciation of chronology and sense of time. Different formats for constructing timelines are shown below.

Ideas for specific timeline activities are given on the photocopiable sheets: Timelines 1, 2 and 3 (pages 75–77).

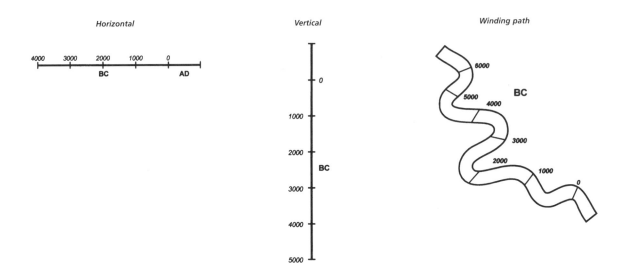

Timelines

Timelines help children understand the correct order in which events happened. They can also highlight the periods of time that elapsed between them. Helping primary-aged children to develop a greater awareness of time is one of the most difficult parts of teaching history. Support written tasks by putting up examples of timelines in the classroom so that the children can base their own ideas on these. As already mentioned, focus on sequencing events and characters, and the use of key vocabulary, such as 'before', 'after' and 'about

the same time as'. Older children should also be familiar with words such as 'decade', 'century' and 'millennium'. In this particular topic, 'kingdom', 'period', 'intermediate' and 'dynasty' will also be useful. It should be noted that some reference sources are now using the term Before Common Era (BCE) in place of Before Christ (BC).

NNSF links: Years 3 and 4: Read and begin to write the vocabulary related to time. Read simple timetables. Years 5 and 6: Use units of time.

Ordered Society

Data can sometimes be organised in the form of a hierarchy. A hierarchy is really a pyramid of power in which people are sorted in order of importance. Usually there is one leader at the top, several leading people below them, greater numbers in the next rank, still more below that, and so on. Society in Ancient Egypt was organised very much along the lines of social class. Once you were born into a certain class, you remained there and it was very difficult to move from one class to another. Give the children the following details of the organisation of society in Ancient Egypt.

> The most powerful group of individuals in Egyptian society was the ruling pharoah and members of the royal family. Important nobles and the generals that were in charge of the army followed them and senior high priests and viziers were also included in this group. On the third rung of power came those who were vital for the smooth running and organisation of the country, like scribes, engineers, priests and doctors. Because of the skilful jobs they carried out, craft workers, farmers and bakers came next in the order of things. At the bottom of the list were peasants, labourers and slaves, many of whom were captured in battle when Egypt fought against other countries.

Challenge the children to convert this information into a hierarchy pyramid with each level getting wider as it moves towards the base of the shape. Five levels will be needed.

Figure 14 shows a hierarchy pyramid for the Egyptian army.

Figure 14

Provide large copies of the diagram for the children and ask them to reverse the process by writing a detailed description of the information it shows.

Ordered Society

Discuss with the children the best strategy for converting the information given in the tinted box above into a hierarchy pyramid chart. Suggest they read through the text carefully first and make a rough copy of the hierarchy pyramid. They should then check they have the right number of ranks and that they are in the correct order before making a neat and tidy final copy.

Children who are keen to follow up these activities could find out more about the different roles of the people listed. Why did the pharaoh need a vizier? Why were scribes considered to be important? Were some craftsmen more highly rated than others?

As an extension, the children could make similar charts of the organisation of staff within the school. Alternatively, they might want to compare the system that operated in another ancient civilisation, such as the Aztecs of South America. Others may be interested in looking at the hierarchy of ranks in one of our armed services, such as the army, navy or air force.

NNSF links: Years 3, 4, 5 and 6: Solve a problem by representing, extracting and interpreting data in tables, graphs, charts and diagrams.

Vocabulary Box

armed forces

average

Aztec

bar chart

bar-line chart

border

boundary

capital

Celsius

census

century

chronology

circumference

climate

compass

continent

constant proportion

conversion graph

co-ordinates

cycle

decade

degree

delta

desert

era

Euro

explorer

Fahrenheit

fertile

hierarchy

index

intermediate

inundation

invasion

irrigation

Islamic

kingdom

line graph

Middle East

millennium

period

pie chart

population

protractor

quarry

scale

sector

silt

society

social class

South America

tallying

temperature

timeline

tributary

Captain's Travels

○ Simit is the captain of a trading ship in Ancient Egypt.

○ He travels to other countries with his cargo and brings goods back to Egypt. Here are some of the places he visits:

Syria   **Lebanon**   **Cyprus**   **Greece**   **India**   **Afghanistan**
Punt (Somalia)   **Babylon (Iran)**

○ Using an atlas, find Egypt on the map below and colour it red. Label the River Nile. Find the countries listed above and colour them in. Draw lines to show the journey Simit makes to reach them. What cargo does he take to these countries? What goods does he bring back?

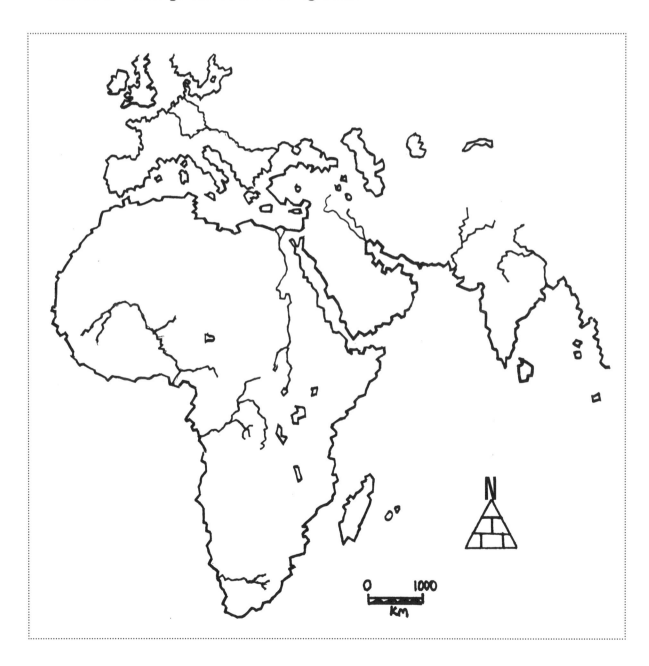

River Deep

○ Egypt's River Nile is the longest river in the world.

○ On the squared paper below, draw a bar-line graph or stick graph to show how the River Nile compares with seven other major rivers in the world.

Nile (Africa) 6,700km   Amazon (South America) 6,600km
Chang Jiang (China) 6,300km Mississippi-Missouri (USA) 6,000km
Ob-Irtysk (Siberia) 5,600km Huang He (China) 5,500km
Zaire (Africa) 4,500km   Mekong (Vietnam) 4,400km

○ You will need to think carefully about the scale you use even though the distances have been rounded off for you. Remember to label the graph fully and interpret it when you have finished.

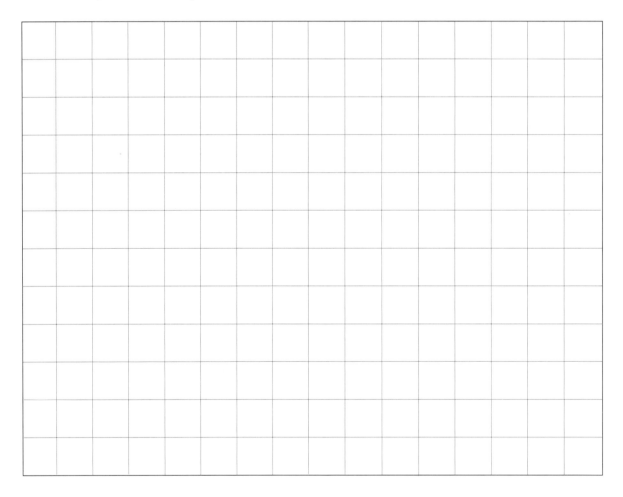

○ More research: find out which are the longest rivers in Britain. How do they compare with the length of the River Nile?

Holiday Travel

○ Tourists from all over Europe travel to Egypt to visit historic sites like the pyramids, the tombs, the temples and the museums.

○ On the map below, show the routes used to fly from these European capital cities to Cairo in Egypt.

London   Paris   Rome   Madrid   Moscow   Dublin   Athens   Berlin

○ More research: use an atlas to work out the distances between each of the capital cities and Cairo. If a jumbo jet travels at an average of 800km per hour, use the formula *speed = distance ÷ time* to work out approximately how long each of the flights will last.

Sunny Weather

○ They have lots of hot sunny weather in Egypt and very little rain all year round.

○ Here are the average monthly temperatures for Egypt's capital city Cairo.

January 19°C	February 21°C	March 24°C	April 28°C
May 29°C	June 30°C	July 32°C	August 33°C
September 28°C	October 27°C	November 29°C	December 21°C

○ Plot them on the squared paper below to make a line graph. Label the graph fully and then answer the questions below.

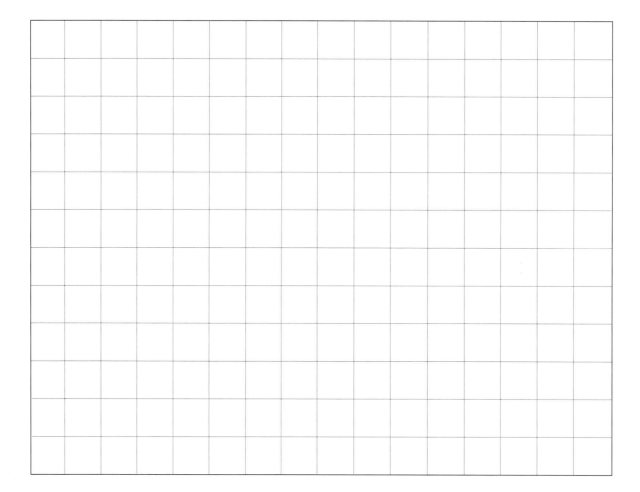

○ Which is the hottest month?
○ Which is the coolest month?
○ Which months have the same temperature?
○ Which month would you like to visit Egypt? Give reasons for your answer.

Hotter or Cooler?

○ It is usually very hot in Egypt, but temperatures can vary from one part of the country to another. The average temperature each month in Luxor is usually higher than that in Cairo. Explain why this is the case.

○ Here are the average monthly temperatures for the two places. Plot them both using separate line graphs on the grid provided. Use a different coloured pencil to show each one. Label the graph fully and then answer the questions below.

Cairo

January 19°C	February 21°C	March 24°C	April 28°C
May 29°C	June 30°C	July 32°C	August 33°C
September 28°C	October 27°C	November 29°C	December 21°C

Luxor

January 23°C	February 26°C	March 30°C	April 35°C
May 40°C	June 41°C	July 42°C	August 41°C
September 39°C	October 37°C	November 31°C	December 26°C

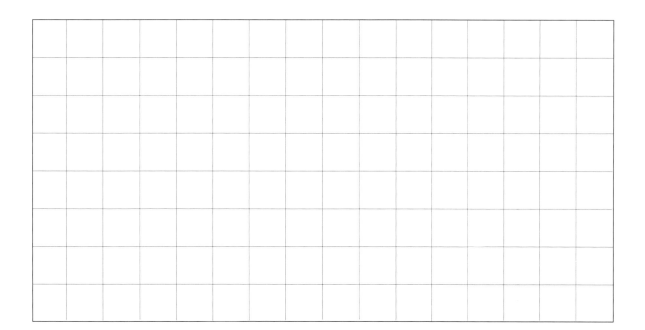

○ When and where is the highest temperature?
○ When and where is the coolest temperature?
○ What time of the year is the hottest in both locations?
○ What time of the year is the coolest in both locations?
○ When and where would you like to visit Egypt? Give reasons for your answer.

Cairo or London?

○ You are going to make line graphs to show the difference between the average monthly temperatures in the capital cities of London in England and Cairo in Egypt.

○ Below is the information you need. Plot the graphs separately on the grid provided. Join the points in each one to show how the temperature rises and falls. Remember to label the graphs fully.

Cairo

January 19°C	February 21°C	March 24°C	April 28°C
May 29°C	June 30°C	July 32°C	August 33°C
September 28°C	October 27°C	November 29°C	December 21°C

London

January 8°C	February 10°C	March 11°C	April 13°C
May 14°C	June 17°C	July 18°C	August 18°C
September 15°C	October 13°C	November 11°C	December 8°C

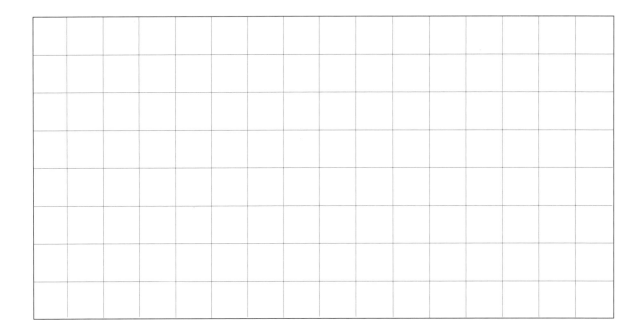

○ Now write six things that the graphs tell you about the temperatures in both the countries. Which months are most similar? Which months show the greatest contrast?

Key Dates

○ Here are the names and dates of some of the main events in the history of Ancient Egypt.

○ Put them in the correct sequence on the timeline below. Use arrows to show their positions and label each one carefully.

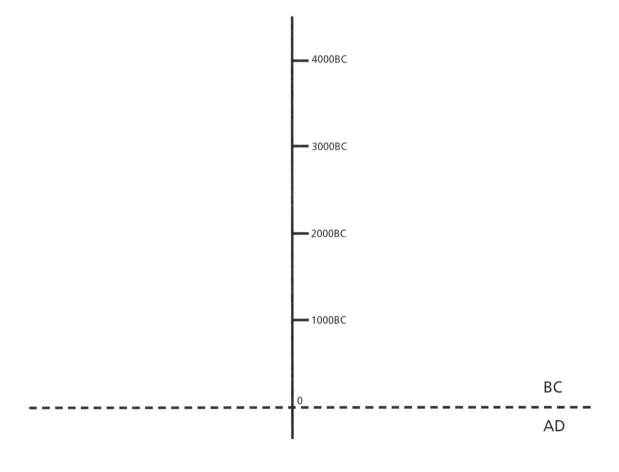

The Battle of Kadesh 1285BC
Building the Great Pyramid 2530BC
Alexander the Great invades Egypt 332BC
Roman armies invade Egypt 30BC
Tutankhamun dies 1323BC
First pharaoh of united Egypt 3100BC
First settlers arrive in Egypt 4000BC
Papyrus first used for writing 2900BC

4000BC

3000BC

2000BC

1000BC

0

BC

AD

○ Now find out as much as you can about the events and the people on your timeline.

Period Piece

○ In about 300BC a priest named Manetho tried to split the history of Ancient Egypt into manageable periods of time. He gave them special names like 'The Old Kingdom' and 'The Late Period'.

○ Here is a simplified version of his work. Some dates have been rounded off to make things easier. Shade in a block for each period on the blank timeline below. Use different colours and label each period carefully.

> Predynastic Period 3500–3200BC
> Early Dynastic Period 3200–2700BC
> The Old Kingdom 2700–2180BC
> First Intermediate Period 2180–2040BC
> The Middle Kingdom 2040–1640BC
> Second Intermediate Period 1640–1570BC
> The New Kingdom 1570–1080BC
> The Late Period 1080–330BC
> The Greek-Roman Period 330–30BC

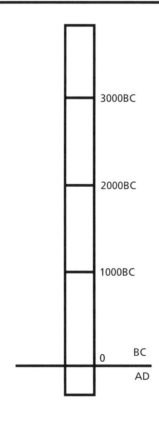

○ Further research: try to find out about something that happened in each of these periods of time.

Long History

○ Ten of the most important events in the history of Ancient Egypt are given below with the dates of when they happened.

○ Draw a timeline to show these events using any style you want. Give it a suitable scale and position the events in the correct sequence. Remember that with BC dates, you start with the highest number and go down in size towards zero – for example, 4000BC, 3500BC, 3000BC, 2500BC and so on.

EVENTS

The Battle of Kadesh 1285BC

First settlers in Egypt 4000BC

Building the Great Pyramid 2530BC

Roman armies invade Egypt 30BC

Chariots first used 1640BC

Tutankhamun dies 1323BC

First pharaoh of united Egypt 3100BC

Papyrus first used 2900BC

Hieroglyphic writing starts 3000BC

Alexander the Great captures Egypt 332BC.

○ Now find out as much as you can about each of these events.

Measures, Shape and Space

Pyramid builders

Egypt's most famous pyramids, built some 4,500 years ago, are the only remaining survivors of the seven wonders of the ancient world and they remain the oldest stone buildings still in existence. Early pyramids, called mastaba after the Arabic word for 'bench', appear to have been raised stone blocks to protect underground tombs from grave robbers. These were followed by stepped pyramids, like the one built for the Pharaoh Djoser at Sakkara (2630BC), and the bent pyramid. Eventually, they developed into the familiar shape we know today when the burial chamber and other rooms were moved from underground to inside the structure.

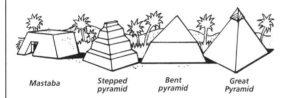

Mastaba   *Stepped pyramid*   *Bent pyramid*   *Great Pyramid*

The true pyramid age really dawned with the building of the Great Pyramid at Giza as the burial place for the ruler Khufu in around 2530BC. It is 140m high and its sides are 230m long at the base. Over two million limestone blocks, weighing between 2.5 and 15 tonne, are thought to have been used in its construction – they could be used to build a low boundary around the world. Over 100 000 workers, although probably only 40 000 on a full-time basis, were employed in its building, which took over 20 years.

All of this construction work took place without pulley systems and heavy lifting gear. Gangs of workmen appear to have used sledges, rollers and ramps to move blocks of stone which were cut into shape at nearby quarries with chisels, axes, wedges and mallets and then floated across the Nile. Set-squares and plumb-lines were used so accurately in the Great Pyramid to determine angles and straight lines that the outer casing blocks fit so snugly a knife blade cannot be pushed between them.

Centuries later, other civilisations, like the Aztec and the Mayan, also built pyramids. These usually had steps or terraces rising to a flat top and were mainly for religious ceremonies. In more modern times, too, the pyramid shape has achieved something of a renaissance. Examples include the glass and steel girder construction at the entrance to the Louvre in Paris, the Canary Wharf Tower in London, which is topped with a pyramid shape, and the Transamerica Pyramid office block in San Francisco.

Measuring up

When it came to devising a system of length measurement, the Ancient Egyptians looked no further than something that was both easy to use and very relevant to them as individuals – the human body. The main unit was the cubit – the distance from the elbow to the tip of the middle finger. In metric terms, this was about 50cm, depending on the individual. The Egyptians also used smaller units. There was the digit, the width of the first finger at the knucklebone (2cm), the palm (not including the thumb) which was four digits (8cm), and the span, three palms (24cm). Four cubits (roughly 200cm) were reckoned to make a stature – the distance from the longest finger to longest finger with the arms outstretched. For longer measurements, the hayt was used. This was 100 cubits. Land areas were most commonly calculated in aroura, which was equal to the area of a square whose side was 100 cubits, that is 10 000 square cubits.

Since individuals varied in size, the cubit, sometimes referred to as the royal cubit, may have originally been based on the dimensions of the pharaoh. The usual cubit measure was a wooden stick or rod that would also be marked with the smaller divisions. The fact that measurements were linked to the pharaoh may help to explain our use of the word 'ruler' for measuring equipment. Scribes measuring long distances like field boundaries probably used ropes knotted at cubit intervals.

Mass or weight was measured in deben, the equivalent today of about 90g. A tenth of this was a kite. Dry measures, like barley and wheat, were placed in jars and pots but were calculated in hekats – about a gallon or just over four and half litres. The smaller unit or hin was about half a litre. Graded jugs were used for working out the capacity of liquids in des-jugs, believed by one source to also be about half a litre.

Because the Ancient Egyptians had no currency system and business and trade depended on barter and exchange, it was important that weights and measures were accurate. There is evidence that they were checked regularly by government officials and that anyone found cheating was severely punished. The Egyptians had no prison system as such, but wrongdoers were often banished to neighbouring countries or sent to labour camps. Boundary markers that showed the extent of fields owned by individual farmers were also inspected by officials frequently as field size was used to determine how much of the crop would need to be given in government taxes each year.

Measures, Shape and Space

The Pyramids

Working with nets can help children to understand the basics of pyramid construction. Provide isometric and dotted paper and challenge the children to find as many nets as possible, firstly for the triangular-based pyramid (tetrahedron) and then the square-based version familiar in Egypt. It may be possible to make actual scaled-down versions of the Great Pyramid at Giza. Models have been found in Egypt by archaeologists but there is no way of knowing whether they were made before or after the original. Encourage the children to compare and contrast the two types of pyramid. In what ways are they similar and different? How many faces do they have and what shapes are they? How many edges are there? How many corners do they have?

With construction or art straws and sticky tape, ask the children to construct skeletal versions of these two 3D shapes (see Figure 1). The construction of mastabas and stepped pyramids from nets would provide children with the chance to work on other 3D shapes, like cubes, cuboids and triangular prisms.

Tetrahedron (triangular-based)   Egyptian pyramid (square-based)

Figure 1

Practical activities based particularly on the Egyptian pyramid can be found on photocopiable sheets: Pyramids 1, 2 and 3 (pages 88–90).

The Pyramids

For information, the tetrahedron has four triangular faces, six edges and four corners or vertices, while the Egyptian pyramid has four triangular faces, one square face, eight edges and five corners. The tetrahedron belongs to the family known as the Five Platonic Polyhedra because all its faces are the same shape and size. The Egyptian pyramid, of course, does not fit these criteria. Making skeletal shapes is particularly helpful for children who have difficulty calculating the number of edges and corners in 3D shapes. Edges have to be measured and cut before construction and corners become fixing points.

There are several possible extension activities here. Two Egyptian pyramids joined at the square base, for example, form an octahedron – a shape that also belongs to the family of Platonic Polyhedra because it has eight identical triangular faces. The net for making it as a single shape is shown in the diagram opposite. Details in the Rhind Papyrus show that the Egyptians calculated the volume of a pyramid as one-third multiplied by the area of the base multiplied by the height, although they had no way of proving this. They also found that if a

pyramid is cut vertically along the diagonals of its base, four smaller but identical solids will be produced. This is used in the Rhind Papyrus to show how the height of a pyramid is directly related to the size and angle of slope of each triangular face. Children could investigate this.

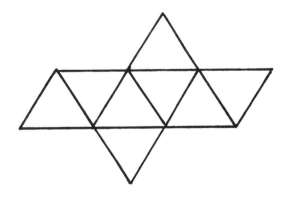

NNSF links: Year 3: *Classify and describe 3D shapes. Relate solid shapes to pictures of them.* Year 4: *Describe and visualise 3D shapes including the tetrahedron. Identify simple nets of solid shapes.* Year 5: *Make shapes with increasing accuracy. Visualise 3D shapes from 2D drawings.* Year 6: *Describe and visualise properties of solid shapes such as faces and edges.*

Right Angles

Their beliefs about the sun and the stars gave the Ancient Egyptians a strong desire to align the position of their square-based pyramids along the four main compass points. They found the north–south line relatively easy to find by using shadows cast by the sun. But the east–west line could only be discovered by making a line that was at right angles to the north–south one. They solved the problem and so found the right angles needed for the four corners of the pyramid's base by using a rope stretching technique in which ropes were divided into sections using knots. Skilled rope fasteners, who divided ropes into sections that had the correct ratios, were used so that errors were kept to a minimum. To make sure the base of the pyramid was level, the Egyptians used a system of trenches filled with water. Water will find its own level so when the water line was marked it gave them a horizontal level over the whole area.

Practical investigations involving these methods are provided on the photocopiable sheets: Right angles 1, 2 and 3 (pages 91–93).

Right Angles

In the case of the 3, 4, 5 triangle shown on right angles 2 and 3 (pages 92–93), the squares on the two shorter sides are equal to the square on the third or longest side known as the hypotenuse ($3^2 + 4^2 = 5^2$ or $9 + 16 = 25$). Provided that the length of the sides of this triangle are increased in the same proportion, a right angle will always be produced. It does, for example, if the numbers are doubled to 6, 8 and 10 ($36 + 64 = 100$) or trebled to 9, 12 and 15 ($81 + 144 = 225$). This is now known as Pythagoras' Theorem but the Egyptians certainly did not write it down and it was left to Pythagoras and his followers to do this in around 500BC. The length of the sides of a right-angled triangle need not be numbers in sequence. With the aid of a calculator, challenge the children to find other combinations that work out – for example, 5, 12 and 13 ($25 + 144 = 169$) and 7, 24 and 25 ($49 + 576$ = 625$). Do the solutions fit any kind of pattern? Use the opportunity to work on other important vocabulary connected with angles, such as 'acute', 'obtuse' and 'reflex'. Also provide tasks that will encourage children to establish important angle facts like the following: A triangle can only ever have one right angle. The angles in a triangle always total 180 degrees. The angles in a quadrilateral always total 360 degrees. Finally, consider the importance of right angles in construction and building today.

NNSF links: Year 3: Identify right angles. Compare angles with a right angle. Year 4: Begin to know that angles are measured in degrees. Start to order a set of angles less than 180 degrees. Year 5: Understand and use angle measure in degrees. Identify, estimate and order acute and obtuse angles. Calculate angles in a straight line. Year 6: Recognise and estimate angles. Check that the sum of the angles of a triangle is 180 degrees.

Body Measures

Details of the body measurements used by the Ancient Egyptians are given in Fact box 2 on page 78. The photocopiable sheets: Measures 1, 2 and 3 (pages 94–96) give children the opportunity to see how well this system operates in practice.

Ask the children to make a cubit measuring stick from their own dimensions that could be used for measuring tasks around the classroom. This could be made from a narrow strip of wood, such as a dowel rod. Smaller units could be marked on it like digits, palms or spans, in the same way that today's centimetre rulers are divided into millimetres. Alternatively, a similar measuring device could be made from a narrow strip of thick card. This would have much more flexibility when checking dimensions on irregular shaped objects.

The children may also be interested to learn that Britain has its own system of body measures that developed into the imperial system of measurement that is still preferred by some adults. Britain's own system originated in the reign of the English king Henry I (1100–1135) and was based on the monarch's own physique. From the nose to the tip of the outstretched arm was the yard. Henry's height, called a stature, was reckoned to be two yards. They measured the king's foot and found that one yard was equivalent to three feet. The foot was then divided into 12 inches and the hand into four inches. Some children may know that the height of a horse is still measured in hands and that the depth of water at sea is measured in fathoms, which is the same as one stature or six feet. Encourage the children to make comparisons between the Egyptian and British systems. Also discuss the main disadvantages of using these systems, especially the wide variations that exist from person to person. This is the main reason why they have been replaced by a system of international standardised (SI) units

NNSF links: Year 3: Read and begin to write the vocabulary related to length. Suggest suitable units and measuring equipment to estimate or measure length. Year 4: Know and use the relationships between familiar units of length. Suggest suitable units and measuring equipment to estimate and measure length. Years 5 and 6: Know imperial units. Suggest suitable units and measuring equipment to estimate and measure length.

Tall Objects

Greek mathematicians like Thales (624–547BC) who visited the Pyramids many centuries after they were built were anxious to find out how tall they were. Thales developed a method of finding the height of tall objects, like pyramids, temples and obelisks, by using shadows. He measured the shadow of the tall object when his own shadow was the length of himself. He then used knowledge of his own height to work out the missing measurement (Figure 2).

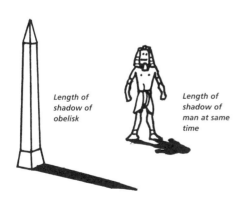

Length of shadow of obelisk

Length of shadow of man at same time

Figure 2

Try out this slightly different method with the children. When the sun is shining, put a metre stick upright in the ground and measure its shadow. Measure the length of shadow of a tall object, like the school building. With the aid of a calculator, divide the length of the object's shadow by the length of the stick's shadow. The answer will be the approximate height of the object in metres.

Also talk to the children about the Egyptians' use of a Nilometer – a device for checking the depth of the river. Set up some simple experiments using a water container for the children to do under supervision. Chart the progress of the watermark up the measure as liquid is added to the container.

Reinforce the bar-line or stick graph work outlined in the last chapter to compare the height of the pyramids with other tall buildings in the world. See the data provided on heights of buildings in the teacher's notes on page 82.

The shadow method suggested for use in school is based on the fact that the ratio of the stick to its shadow is the same as the ratio of the height of the object to its shadow.

For information, obelisks are tall, thin stone pillars that have tapering sides. They were often erected in front of temples and tombs with identifying detail carved on the sides. The top was usually finished off with a small pyramid called a pyramidion and these were sometimes covered with gold to reflect the rays of the sun (see diagram).

Pyramidion sometimes covered in gold

Top of obelisk

Two of the world's most well known obelisks are those originally built by the Pharaoh Thutmose II at Heliopolis. During Roman times they were moved to Alexandria and then shipped to Europe. The one known as Cleopatra's Needle was erected on the Thames Embankment in 1878 and the other in Central Park, New York, two years later.

Originally, the Egyptians inserted measuring posts into the bed of the River Nile at intervals along the bank so they could check the water levels at the start of each flood season. Later, stone stairways were cut down into the riverbank so more accurate measurements could be taken. By watching how long it took for the water to cover each step, they could calculate how fast the floods were rising and predict how high they would reach.

The heights of famous buildings in the world that could be compared to the Great Pyramid at Giza include St Paul's Cathedral (110m), the Arc de Triomphe (49.5m) and the Statue of Liberty (92m). These, however, are dwarfed by more modern constructions such as the CN Tower in Toronto (553m) and the Sears Building in Chicago (443m).

NNSF links: Year 3: Measure and compare using standard units and draw and measure lines to the nearest half centimetre. Year 4: Use, read and write standard metric units including their abbreviations. Year 5: Use, read and write standard metric units including their abbreviations and relationships. Convert larger to smaller units. Year 6: As Year 5. Also convert smaller to larger units and vice versa.

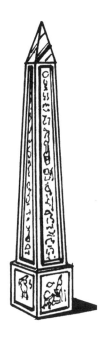

More Measures

Reference sources are divided over the exact modern equivalents of many of the main units of measurement used in Ancient Egypt. They may all be correct because over a period of thousands of years and in a large country divided into regions, change and revision is sure to have taken place a number of times. For these activities, the children can either use the units suggested in Fact box 2 on page 78 or they can use those located during their own research.

Set up weighing activities where the children have to check the weights printed on packets and containers taking the 'e' factor (see notes below) into account (Figure 3). Ask the children how many deben these items would be.

Figure 3

Then challenge the children to find the volume of a range of 3D prisms in hins by using dry measures like rice or sand (Figure 4).

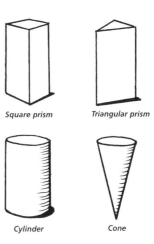

Square prism   Triangular prism

Cylinder   Cone

Figure 4

Finally, ask the children to estimate and then measure how many des-jugs it takes to fill a variety of different containers with water (Figure 5).

Figure 5

More Measures

Discuss with the children the metric units system they normally use and the type of measuring units used by the Ancient Egyptians. Make sure they understand the principle of standard and non-standard measurement and the different kinds of equipment used. Talk about how the measurements mentioned in Fact box 2 would have been used by ordinary people in everyday life in Ancient Egypt. Examine the type of packaging used particularly for food items these days and how weights and measures have to be clearly marked. How does this compare with the Egyptian method of using mainly pottery jars in different sizes for determining food item amounts like wheat, barley, olives, figs, nuts, beer and wine? The letter 'e' on modern packaging stands for excluding and means the weight of the food item inside the packaging but not including the weight of the tin, jar, carton, box or wrapping. Occasionally, the words gross and net are still used. Gross weight is the weight of a container and its contents while net weight is the weight of what is inside the container only.

NNSF links: Year 3: Suggest suitable units and measuring equipment to estimate or measure mass and capacity. Read scales to the nearest division.
Years 4, 5 and 6: As Year 3. Also record estimates and readings from scales to a suitable degree of accuracy.

Area and Perimeter

Both the Rhind Mathematical Papyrus and the Moscow Mathematical Papyrus contain examples of calculations carried out by the Ancient Egyptians involving finding the area of both rectangles and triangles. Evidence shows scribes worked largely with the formulae we use now, finding the area of rectangles by multiplying the length by the width and triangles by halving the product of the base and the height. Extend the children's calculation skills by encouraging them to find the area of compound shapes in which they need to work out some of the dimensions for themselves (Figure 6).

Alternatively, set the children to work on problems using large units of measurements. For example, ask them which room in the school has the largest area, how the area of a long, thin corridor compares with the area of a small, almost square room, what the area of the playground is, and what the area of the playing field is.

Take the opportunity to include perimeter measurements as well. Ask the children to work out the area of the Great Pyramid at Giza in both hectares and acres. However, since each of the sides measure 213m, mapping out and demonstrating this area in practical terms may be difficult unless a large field is easily available.

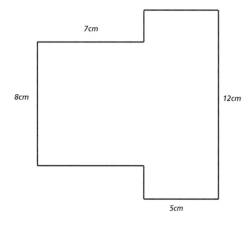

Figure 6

Area and Perimeter

Establish first of all that the children appreciate the difference between area and perimeter. Area is the amount of surface in a shape and is measured in square units. Perimeter is the distance around the outside of a shape and is calculated as a distance. Point out to the children the flexibility of the formula for finding the area of a rectangle.

> **area of rectangle (a) = length (l) x width (w)**
> **so l = a÷w and w = a÷l**

Encourage the children to make sensible choices when choosing equipment for calculating areas outside – for example, long tape measures and trundle wheels. Inform the children that working out the area of a farmer's field regularly in Ancient Egypt was important for two main reasons. It not only affected the scale of taxes that had to be paid but also re-established the correct amount of land due if some had recently been washed away by floodwater.

NNSF links: Years 3 and 4: Measure and calculate the area and perimeter of rectangles and other simple shapes. Year 5: Understand and use the formula area = length x width for the area of a rectangle. Understand, measure and calculate the perimeters of rectangles and regular polygons. Year 6: Calculate the area and perimeter of simple compound shapes that can be split into rectangles.

Grid Drawings

Egyptian artists used an accurately drawn grid system to ensure their carvings, sculptures and paintings were in the correct proportions. Strict rules controlled the measurements used on these grids. Major works of art were first drawn in sketch form on boards and then later transferred to larger surfaces. Let the children try out some of the problems the Ancient Egyptians must have encountered by setting some drawing problems on squared paper. Challenge them to draw shapes or simple pictures on a small grid, say 1cm squared paper, and then increase the same item accurately in size onto a larger grid, such as 2cm squares or 5cm squares.

Also experiment by changing the proportions of the grid system so that shapes are still accurately drawn but become distorted. For example, a grid of tall thin rectangles will produce a picture of a tall thin object (Figure 7).

There are considerable possibilities here to link and extend this kind of work into further tasks involving plotting positions using co-ordinates within a grid system.

The grids used can be of squares or rectangles but all the shapes in each separate grid must be kept exactly the same size and shape. It may help if the grid system is numbered or lettered to help with the location of lines and some children will benefit if various grids are prepared and printed out in advance. Start with simple pyramids, obelisks and palm trees and graduate to more difficult items such as camels and Egyptian characters.

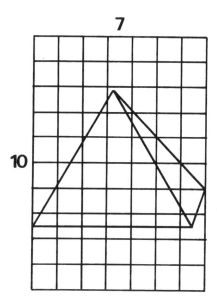
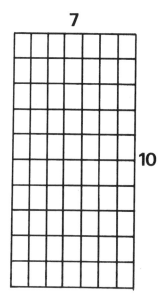

Figure 7

Grid Drawings

It would take a team of artists to work on a major painting found inside a pharaoh's tomb. A plasterer would smooth the wall by spreading on a thin layer of plaster. The surface would then be marked with a square grid using string dipped in red ochre. Outline designers would then use black paint to transfer the original small-scale drawing onto the wall. Stonemasons would chip out the main figures from the background and painters would finally add the detailed colouring necessary. Artists usually drew body parts side on while shoulders and eyes are often drawn as if seen from the front. Key characters are often shown in much larger dimensions. Paintings feature ordinary people carrying out their everyday tasks and this detail has helped historians to piece together Ancient Egypt life.

NNSF links: Year 3: Read and begin to write the vocabulary related to position. Year 4: Describe and find the position of a point on a grid of squares where the lines are numbered. Year 5: Read and plot co-ordinates in the first quadrant. Year 6: Read and plot co-ordinates in all four quadrants.

The Calendar

It has already been pointed out that the Egyptians based their three seasons on the state of the River Nile (see Fact box 2 on page 59). The rest of their calendar calculations were based on the rising and setting of the sun each day and the waxing and the waning of the moon each month. Each season had four months, each month three weeks, and each week ten days. This gave a total of 360 days during the year. The five extra days were added usually at the end of the harvest season although these were considered to be unlucky and were often referred to as demon days. Inaccuracies and variations occurred in time-keeping because no leap year system was in operation.

Encourage the children to use their powers of observation and research skills to chart the rising and setting of the sun during a set period. Local papers will give details about lighting up times. Ask them to contrast the length of hours of daylight and darkness during our four seasons. They could keep detailed records of the phases of the moon during a month, although cloudy skies may prevent observation on some nights.

Help the children to become familiar with using our own calendar. Which months have 30 or 31 days and what special rules apply to February? How many Wednesdays are there in May in 2003? Was 1992 a leap year? How many different ways are there of writing the date? Which are most common? How long is it between 21 June and 3 September? Which festivals fall on set days – for example, Bonfire Night, and which vary each year – for example, Easter Monday? When are bank holidays held and why do we celebrate them?

Using a calculator, children should be able to solve some time problems involving big numbers. On your eleventh birthday how many days have you lived? How many hours do children work in school in a week, a term, a school year? How many years are there in a million days?

The Calendar

The children will soon realise that the Ancient Egyptians based their time system on the cycle of nature they observed around them. They noted the state of the River Nile, the growth of plants and the habits of animals, the movement of the moon and the stars, and the rising and setting of the sun. Examples of calendars have been found in temples and tombs in Egypt and one of the best examples is carved on a wall in the temple of Sibeh and Horus at Kam Ombo. These often show the days of religious festivals. There could be as many as 60 religious holidays during a year. Some indicate the birthday of gods like Seth, the bringer of storms, as this was reckoned to be an unlucky day. Many official documents in Ancient Egypt were dated according to the year number of the ruling Pharaoh at that time, then the season followed by the day. An example might read Year 15, 2nd month of Akhet, day 9'. Challenge the children to work out a similar dating system based on the reign of Queen Elizabeth II.

NNSF links: Years 3, 4, 5 and 6: Use a calendar.

Vocabulary Box

acute angle	leap year	Pythagoras' Theorem
area	length	quadrilateral
barter	mass	quality control
calendar	mastaba	reflex angle
capacity	metric system	season
co-ordinates	net	SI units
cube	Nilometer	span
cubit	non-standard units	statistician
cuboid	obelisk	stature
currency	obtuse angle	tetrahedron
edges	octahedron	triangular prism
face	palm	tonne
formula	perimeter	vertex (vertices)
gross	Platonic Polyhedra	wane
hypotenuse	pyramid	wax
imperial system	pyramidion	weight

In The Net

○ These are two nets for making Egyptian pyramids

○ Add flaps to the nets (one has been added for you) to help with fixing, then cut them out and construct the pyramids using glue.

○ Were your flaps in the right place?

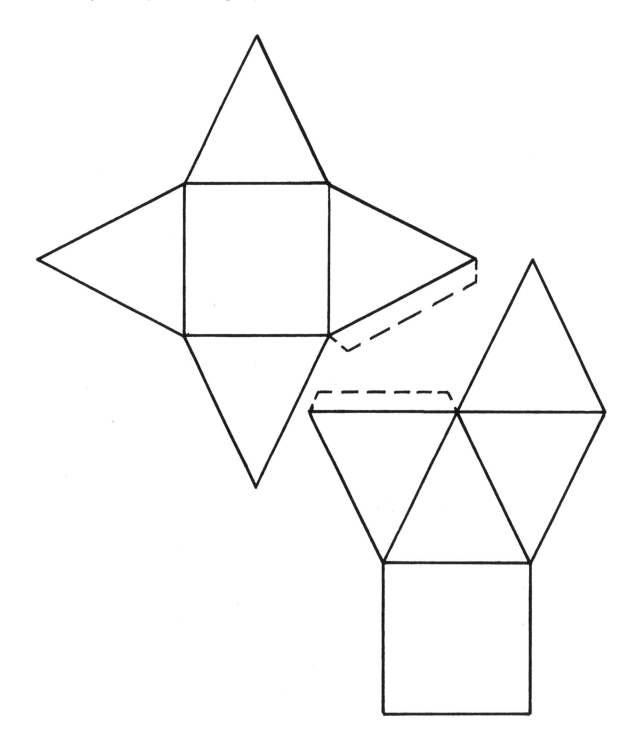

Shape Quiz

○ Hori, the designer and builder, wants to make a small model pyramid before he starts to construct a full-scale tomb for his pharaoh.

○ Look carefully at the nets below. Which one(s) will he need to use to make the pyramid model?

○ Draw each of the nets on thick paper or card, complete with flaps for gluing. Then cut them out, build the models and see if you were right.

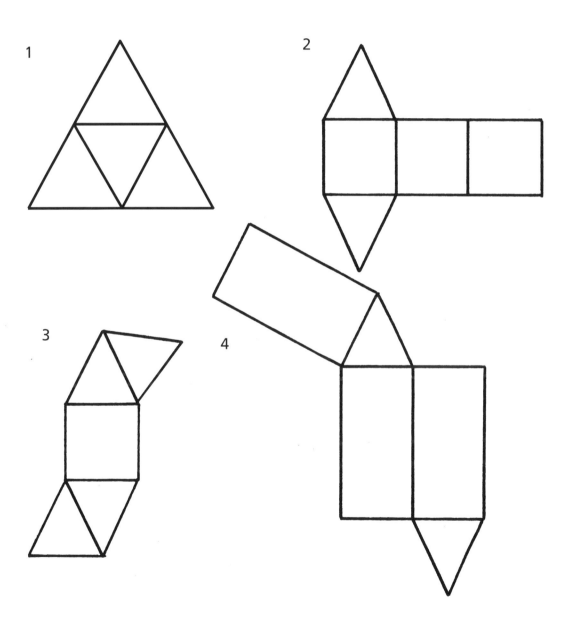

○ Find out more about any other shapes that you have made. What are their names? What are their properties?

Euler's Law

○ The Swiss mathematician Leonhard Euler discovered a rule for 3D shapes like the tetrahedron (triangular-based pyramid) and the Egyptian pyramid (square-based).

○ The rule says that in any 3D shape, edges = faces + vertices − 2.

○ Make small models of the tetrahedron and Egyptian pyramid from thin card and test out the rule. Record your results in the table below. Choose three other straight-sided 3D shapes and also check out the rule with them.

Shape	Faces	Vertices	Faces and vertices	Edges
1 Tetrahedron				
2 Egyptian pyramid				
3				
4				
5				

○ Extension: does this version of Euler's Law also work?

faces + vertices = edges + 2

Put It To The Test

○ A team of Egyptian rope stretchers has been trying to make right-angled triangles before builders start work on the pyramids.

○ Find a way of testing these triangles to see if they have a right angle in them.

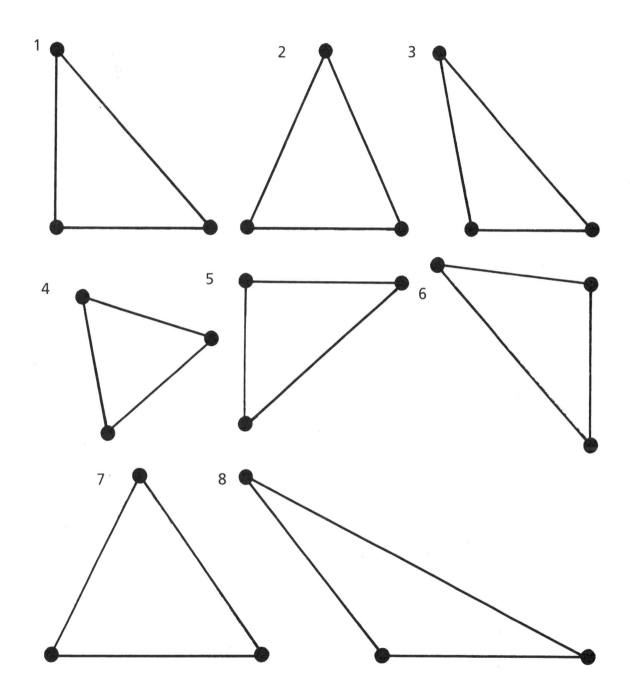

○ How did you test the triangles?
○ How many right angles can a triangle have?
○ What do the angles in a triangle always add up to?

Rope Stretchers

○ Hunefer and his team of architects are planning the base of a new pyramid. They want to make sure the square base has accurate right angles. They will use the rope stretching method. Try out the method they used to see if it produces a right angle.

○ Work outside on the playground or the school field. Take some skipping ropes and tie them together. Mark off lengths of three units, four units and five units with coloured bands (see diagram below). Choose your own units. Each unit could be one metre, two metres or even longer. It depends on the amount of space you have.

3 units   4 units   5 units

○ Now shape the rope to form a triangle and fix it into place with pegs. Have three units as the base and five units as the longest side (see diagram).

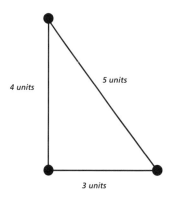

4 units   5 units   3 units

○ Which of the three angles is the right angle?

○ Would you still get a right-angled triangle if you doubled the units? Try six units, eight units and ten units.

○ Try putting two triangles together to make the square base that the pyramid builders needed.

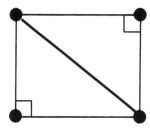

Square Base

○ Egyptian architects always needed to make sure the square base of a pyramid contained accurate right angles.

○ They used a rope stretching method to make these right angles.

○ This one uses the units 3, 4 and 5 to form the right angle.

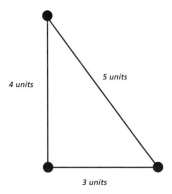

○ The sum of the squares on the two short sides equal the square on the third side.

$$3^2 + 4^2 = 5^2$$

$$9 + 16 = 25$$

○ On large sheets of paper, use a compass and a ruler to draw these triangles accurately to see if they contain a right angle. Then use a calculator to check your results.

Triangle 1: 6cm, 8cm, 10cm

Triangle 2: 4cm, 5cm, 6cm

Triangle 3: 5cm, 8cm, 12cm

Triangle 4: 5cm, 12cm, 13cm

Triangle 5: 8cm, 10cm, 15cm

Body Building

○ Over four thousand years ago, the Ancient Egyptians used their hands and bodies for measuring.

○ The box below gives details of the measures they used and their approximate metric equivalents, rounded off.

digit = (2cm)
palm = 4 digits (8cm)
span = 3 palms (24cm)
cubit = 2 spans (48cm)
stature = 4 cubits (192cm)

○ With the help of a friend and a tape, measure your own digit, palm, span, cubit and stature in centimetres. Record your results in a table like the one below. Do four of your digits = a palm? Do four of your cubits = a stature?

Name	Digit	Palm	Span	Cubit	Stature

○ Repeat the measures on your friend. How do they compare with your own?

○ Do adults have measurements that are closer to those of the Ancient Egyptians?

Round the School

○ In Ancient Egypt, one of the most important measures of length was the cubit – the distance from a person's elbow to the tip of the longest finger.

○ Sometimes it was known as the royal cubit and may have been based on the actual measurement of the pharaoh.

○ Use a piece of rope or string to make a cubit measure. It could be 48cm long or you could use your own cubit measurement. Get a friend to help you.

○ Now use the cubit length to measure some distances around the school. Try the length and width of your classroom, the width of the hall, the length of a corridor, the perimeter of the playground. For some of the longer distances, you could use the hayt, which was equal to 100 cubits. Also measure the distances in metres and centimetres with a tape or a trundle wheel to see how the two methods compare.

○ Record your results in the table below.

Distance measured	Cubits	Metric measures

Great Goliath

○ The Ancient Egyptians used the cubit as one of their main units of length measurement. It was the distance from the elbow to the tip of the longest finger on an adult. It was reckoned to be about 48cm long.

○ Later, the Greeks and the Romans also used the cubit. The Greek cubit was thought to be about 46cm while the Roman cubit was shorter at 44cm.

○ Take some cubit measurements from a group of friends, including some adults. How do they compare? Which of the three measurements above – the Egyptian, the Greek or the Roman – is the closest to your own results?

Here is a short passage from the Old Testament of the Bible. It is about the famous giant Goliath who fought against David.

'And there went out a champion, out of the camp of the Philistines named Goliath … whose height was six cubits and a span.'

○ If a span was the distance from the thumb to the little finger with the hand outstretched, calculate how tall Goliath was according to the Egyptian, Greek and Roman measurement of the cubit.

○ Mark how tall Goliath was on the classroom wall. How does he compare with the children in your class? Would he have been able to get through the classroom door easily?

Answers to photocopiable sheets

Page 12

19   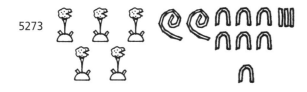

43

89

156

275

14 Nile boats; 68 goats; 256 sheep; 315 stone blocks.

Page 13

76

132

693

1564

5273

81; 3464; 7068

Page 14

Totals: Village 1 – 96; Village 2 – 108; Town 1 – 516; Town 2 – 5,667; Village 3 – 147; Village 4 – 1,899.

Page 18

Third of 12 = 4; Half of 24 = 12; Quarter of 32 = 8; Fifth of 45 = 9; Tenth of 90 = 9; Two-thirds of 15 = 10.

Page 19

1 Eighth, quarter, half, three-quarters.

2 Third, half, five-eighths, three-quarters.

3 Eighth, quarter, three-eighths, half.

Fifth of 35 = 7; two-thirds of 36 = 24; three-quarters of 60 = 45; three-eighths of 64 = 24; nine-tenths of 120 = 108; five-ninths of 117 = 65.

Page 20

Half = quarter + quarter; two-thirds = third + third; three-tenths = fifth + tenth; three-eighths = quarter + eighth; five-sixths = third + third + sixth; four-sevenths = seventh + seventh + seventh + fourteenth + fourteenth.

18	104
28	244
40	3,628

Page 32

19 x 7 = 133; 21 x 8 = 168; 58 x 9 = 522; 83 x 6 = 498.

Page 33

85 x 8 = 680; 96 x 7 = 672; 18 x 15 = 270; 44 x 24 = 1056.

Page 34

28 x 14 = 392; 57 x 34 = 1938; 36 x 21 = 756; 65 x 48 = 3120; 112 ÷ 4 = 28; 245 ÷ 7 = 35; 392 ÷ 8 = 49.

Page 35

1
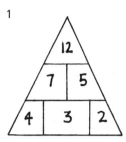

2
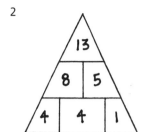

3
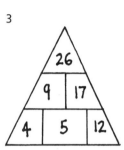

4
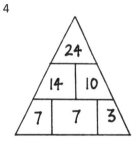

Page 36

1
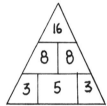

2
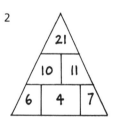

3
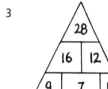

4
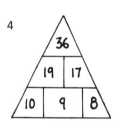

5
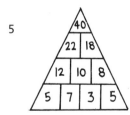

6
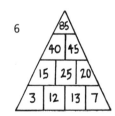

7

Page 37

1
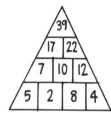

2
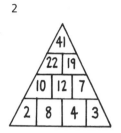

3
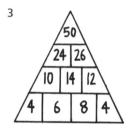

4
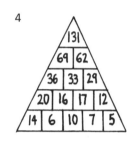

5
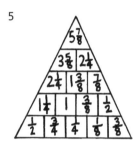

6
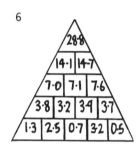

Page 38

£5 = 30; £12.50 = 75; £15 = 90; £35 = 210; £48 = 288; £52 = 312; £60.50 = 363; £86 = 516.

Page 39

Mary 90; David 180; Joanne 198; Mum 2,700; Dad 3,600.

Page 40

Costs for the family are Hotel Pyramid £2,295; Hotel Nile £2,433.40; Hotel Sphinx £3,075.60 and Hotel Pharaoh £2,453. The most expensive is the Hotel Sphinx and the cheapest the Hotel Pyramid.

Page 50

Grain harvest: 15 + 24 = 39; 31 + 19 = 50; 59 – 12 = 47; 57 – 45 = 12 then children's own answers.

Date picking: 5 x 8 = 40; 12 x 4 = 48; 15 x 6 = 90; 54 ÷ 9 = 6; then children's own answers.

Wine making: 1: 57; 2: 57; 3: 108; 4: 49.

Page 51

36, 43. Rule: +7

52, 43. Rule: –9

128, 256. Rule: x 2

36, 25. Rule: Square numbers 6 x 6 and 5 x 5

2, 5. Rule: + 3

36, 34. Rule: +5 –2

28, 24. Rule: Subtract 1 less each time

20.2, 21.7. Rule: +1.5

Puzzle: 27 + 40 + 53 = 120 and 1 + 14 = 15 x 8 = 120

Page 52

1: 12; 2: 36; 3: 16; 4: 90

Problem 79: 7 x 7 = 49 x 7 = 343 x 7 = 2,401 x 7 = 16 807 morsels of new grain would be saved.

Page 72

The hottest month is August. The coolest month is January. February and December have the same temperature.

Page 73

The highest temperature is 42°C at Luxor in July. The coolest temperature is 19°C at Cairo in January. July and August are the hottest in both locations. January is the coolest in both locations.

Page 89

Shape 1 will build a tetrahedron. Shape 3 will build an Egyptian squared-based pyramid.

Page 90

The tetrahedron has four faces, four vertices and six edges. The Egyptian pyramid has five faces, five vertices and eight edges. Both versions of the law work for both these shapes and other straight-sided 3D shapes the children have chosen.

Page 91

The triangles with right angles are 1 and 5. A triangle can only have one right angle. The angles in a triangle always total 180 degrees.

Page 93

The right-angled triangles are Triangle 1: 36 + 64 = 100 and Triangle 4: 25 + 144 = 169.

Page 96

If a span is taken as 24cm for each, Goliath would 312cm (3.12m) using the Egyptian cubit, 300cm (3m) using the Greek cubit and 288cm (2.88m) using the Roman cubit. Standard doorways in buildings are about 2m.

Index